D1237590

DISCOURSE ON BODIES IN WATER

No. 2

FACSIMILE REPRINTS in the history of science, sponsored by the History of Science Society of the University of Illinois

GALILEO GALILEI

DISCOURSE ON BODIES IN WATER

Translation by Thomas Salusbury

with Introduction and Notes by
STILLMAN DRAKE

UNIVERSITY OF ILLINOIS PRESS, URBANA, 1960

 Library of Congress Catalog Card No. 60-15930.

Preface

The reprinting of Thomas Salusbury's seventeenth-century translation of this work now, for the first time, makes available simultaneously in English all the principal scientific works of Galileo.

I am particularly indebted to Dr. Max Fisch for setting in motion the sequence of events which have led to this publication.

The very long title that Galileo gave to his book, which is translated in full by Salusbury, has usually given place in ordinary references to the words "Discourse on Floating Bodies" or their equivalents in other languages. That short title, however convenient, is a particularly unfortunate misnomer when considered in the light of the circumstances which led to the composition of the book. Taking advantage of the present relative unfamiliarity of the work in our language, I have used a short title which is more appropriate to the history of the book and to its original name.

To Brother Paul, F.S.C., Head of the Classics Department of Manhattan College, I am deeply indebted not only for the use of the precious volume from which this facsimile has been made, but for assistance and suggestions over a long period of years in my efforts to identify the elusive translator of the text.

I gratefully acknowledge the hours of patient assistance given me by my son Mark in the comparison of Salusbury's text with the definitive Italian edition.

Contents

Introduction

I

Galileo's *Discourse on Bodies in Water* is the least familiar of his scientific works today. At its time it was widely read; indeed, the first edition was so speedily exhausted that Galileo prepared a second, with additions, which was published in the same year. It is the only one of his books that received such treatment at his hands, though most of them were quickly sold out.

For a variety of reasons the present obscurity of the *Discourse* is quite undeserved. It was Galileo's first published contribution to experimental physics, the field in which his enduring fame is securely founded. Hydrostatic researches had, moreover, an intimate connection with the long train of reflections which led him to the first essentially correct ideas of motion that underlie modern mechanics. The earliest of those reflections, preserved in manuscripts which Galileo never published, have recently been presented in English translation for the first time.[1] Only their final fruits, published a quarter of a century after the *Discourse,* have in the past been available in English.[2] Thus the present publication supplies an important link in a chain of events that has hitherto been difficult to examine without a knowledge of both Latin and Italian.

The *Discourse* has also great significance in the formation of that opposition, both scientific and personal, which played so important a part in Galileo's life and in the dissemination of his ideas. It arose from a dispute, notorious at the time, between Galileo and certain professors of philosophy and other adherents of Aristotle who aptly symbolize that combination of ingenious error and authoritarian obstinacy which preceded the rise of modern physics. Of this dispute, Galileo remarked in later years that it had provided him with no wiser or more industrious teacher than ignorance, since to satisfy the ignorance of his opponents he had been driven to the discovery of many conclusions that he pro-

[1] *Galileo on Motion and on Mechanics,* tr. Drabkin and Drake, Madison, 1960.

[2] *Discorsi e Dimostrazione Matematiche . . . ,* Leyden, 1638; trs. Thomas Salusbury, 1665; Thomas Weston, 1730; H. Crew and A. De Salvio, 1914. The last-named translation, currently available in facsimile reprint, is cited hereafter under the title *Two New Sciences.*

ceeded to confirm by new and precise experiments to which he would never have applied himself merely to satisfy his own mind.[3] The story of that dispute and some of its repercussions will be set forth presently.

Although a systematic survey of the literature and history of hydrostatic investigations prior to Galileo cannot be attempted here, some brief remarks touching those points may appropriately be offered. The essential foundations of the science had been established in antiquity in a short but rigorous and elegant treatise by Archimedes.[4] During the middle ages this authentic work of Archimedes was not known, but in its place there was a still briefer and far inferior treatise ascribed to him. This had made its appearance in Europe in the thirteenth century, and remained the standard text on the subject until nearly the time of Galileo's birth.[5] It was first published from a manuscript in the possession of Niccolò Tartaglia, who is said to have been the teacher of Ostilio Ricci, from whom in turn Galileo received his first instruction in mathematics.[6]

About two decades earlier, Tartaglia had published some Latin translations of genuine works of Archimedes, and he had also composed an Italian version of the work on hydrostatics, with commentary.[7] From 1541 to 1551 he had conducted experimental determinations of the relative weights in air and water of a number of substances, which were published in the posthumous volume mentioned above. It was Tartaglia who introduced into Italian an expression for specific gravity (*gravità secondo la specie*), analogous to the Latin phrase that had made its appearance in the pseudo-Archimedean treatise on hydrostatics.[8] New and superior Latin versions of and commentaries on the works of Archimedes were published during the same period by Federico Commandino, who instructed in mathematics Galileo's great patron and friend, the Marquis Guidobaldo dal Monte.[9]

In 1586 the distinguished Flemish mathematician and engineer, Simon Stevin, published a treatise on hydrostatics which went consider-

---

[3] This story is related by Vincenzio Viviani, Galileo's "last pupil" and first biographer; see *Opere* XIX, 613 (all references under this name refer to the National Edition of the works of Galileo edited at Florence by Antonio Favaro).

[4] *The Works of Archimedes,* tr. T. L. Heath [Cambridge, 1897]; Dover Reprint, n.p., n.d., pp. 253-300.

[5] Published with English translation in E. A. Moody and M. Clagett, *The Medieval Science of Weights,* Madison, 1952, pp. 33-53.

[6] *Iordani opusculum de ponderositate* . . . Venice, 1565, pp. 16v.-19v.

[7] *Opera Archimedis . . . per Nicolaum Tartaleam . . . emendata,* Venice, 1543; *Archimedis de insidentibus aquae,* Venice, 1565. The Italian version of the first part of the Archimedean treatise, with commentary, appeared in Tartaglia's *Ragionamenti . . . sopra la sua Travagliata Inventione,* Venice, 1551, where it was accompanied by an Italian paraphrase of the medieval treatise previously mentioned, and by some of Tartaglia's experimental determinations.

[8] *Quesiti et Inventioni Diverse de Nicolo Tartalea,* Venice, 1546, 82v.

[9] *Archimedis opera . . . a Federico Commandino . . . in latinum conversa,* Venice, 1558; *Archimedis de iis quae vehuntur in aqua,* Bologna, 1565.

ably beyond the work of Archimedes.[10] At first relatively inaccessible because it was written in Dutch, this work was translated into Latin in 1605. The style is classic, proceeding from definitions and axioms to theorems and proofs. It is evident that Stevin had performed many experiments, though he did not appeal to them in support of his theorems. His treatise was supplemented by one on the practical side of the subject.[11]

At the beginning of the seventeenth century a detailed treatise on the comparative weights of substances in air and water, with elaborate tables of experimental determinations, was published at Rome by Marino Ghetaldi.[12] The author had been a pupil of Michael Coignet and was acquainted with Galileo, whom he had met at Padua before 1600. In his book, however, he does not mention Tartaglia, Stevin, or Galileo, being presumably unacquainted with their researches in hydrostatics. Ghetaldi's book, like Stevin's, is arranged in the classical deductive style, though it is far more restricted in scope and quite different in purpose.

Of the works mentioned, Galileo certainly knew the genuine treatise of Archimedes. It is very likely that he knew also the medieval treatise, and probably he was acquainted with the *Quesiti* and *Ragionamenti* of Tartaglia and the *Promotus* of Ghetaldi. It is just possible that Galileo had seen the work of Stevin in its Latin translation.[13] He was certainly well versed in the practical knowledge of hydraulics enjoyed by engineers and military men of the period, and this was by no means inconsiderable, particularly in those cities in which Galileo happened to dwell and to work. But the content and method of the *Discourse* do not suggest that Galileo had made any special effort to determine what others had done in the field, or that he cared to adapt to the needs of his dispute the conclusions or procedures of other writers — not even those of Archimedes, whom he admired above all his other predecessors in science and mathematics.

The views of Aristotle concerning the behavior of bodies placed in water, though they occupy a conspicuous place in the dispute, were never set forth in any systematic treatise. It is indeed an exaggeration to attribute to Aristotle the views upheld by Galileo's Peripatetic opponents in this controversy. Characteristically, they had attempted to

[10] *De Beghinselen des Waterwichts,* Engl. tr. C. Dikshoorn, in *The Principal Works of Simon Stevin,* Amsterdam, 1955, I, pp. 376ff.

[11] *Anvang der Waterwichtdaet,* ibid., pp. 482ff.

[12] *Promotus Archimedes seu de variis corporum generibus gravitate magnitudine comparatis,* Rome, 1603.

[13] Giovanni Bardi, who praises Galileo's work in his *Eorum quae vehuntur in aquis experimenta,* Rome, 1614, mentions Stevin. He also adverts to Galileo's expression "specific gravity" as deriving from the medieval treatise published from Tartaglia's papers (n. 6, above). It is more likely that Galileo had in mind the Italian phrase introduced in the *Quesiti,* which must have been familiar to the numerous students of Tartaglia at Venice and Florence.

deduce from some incidental remarks of Aristotle a complete theory of hydrostatics, for these men were wont to defend the lightest word of Aristotle as though that were the only possible basis of science. In the present instance their efforts were particularly inept, and Galileo had the best of them with regard to a principal point of the dispute, inasmuch as Aristotle himself had opened his remarks by saying, "The shape of bodies will not account for their moving upward or downward in general, though it will account for their moving faster or slower."[14]

The *Discourse* is distinguished among works of its time by its repeated recourse to observational and experimental data in opposition to philosophical doctrines. Moreover, the experiments proposed require no elaborate equipment and no technique beyond reasonable patience and care. These facts, coupled with the publication of the work in Italian and the notoriety of the disputes which had led to it, gave the book a great and immediate popularity. The professors who had opposed Galileo felt obliged to defend themselves, and four books were published in reply within a few months. Their authors, together with some other enemies of Galileo's at Florence, banded together in a league against him, the members of which were said to have sworn to oppose whatever he said.

Galileo joked about this self-styled league when he first heard of it, but in time it became no joking matter. At the outset it appears to have consisted of jealous professors and intriguing courtiers, but before long they were joined by members of the clergy intent upon preventing the spread of a belief in the motion of the earth. Thus it came about that the *Discourse,* harmless as it was to religion and society, inspired that organized opposition to Galileo which within a few years gained sufficient strength to hamper seriously his scientific freedom.

II

The dispute over floating bodies which culminated in the writing of the *Discourse* had its origin in July of 1611, not long after Galileo's return to Florence from a triumphant visit to Rome. It should be remembered that Galileo had at that time been less than a year in his post of chief philosopher and mathematician to the Grand Duke of Tuscany, after nearly two decades as professor at the University of Padua in the Venetian Republic. Scarcely more than a year had elapsed since the publication of his startling telescopic discoveries in the *Sidereus Nuncius,* a book that had brought him unprecedented fame, and along with it the usual number of envious rivals.[15] In that book, his first important scientific publication, Galileo had promised his readers that he would shortly publish a treatise on the system of the world, in which it was his intention to support the Copernican view against the prevailing tradi-

[14] *De caelo,* iv. 6 (313a, 14ff.)

[15] Translated as *The Starry Messenger* in S. Drake, *Discoveries and Opinions of Galileo,* N.Y., 1957, pp. 21ff. (Hereafter cited as *Discoveries.*)

tions of astronomy in the universities. It was to this promise that he referred in the opening sentences of the *Discourse*. Subsequent events prevented publication of the promised work until 1632, and brought about his trial and imprisonment for doing so even then.

Galileo was very well acquainted at Florence, where he had spent a considerable part of his youth and to which he had returned during the summer months in several of the years during which he had taught at Padua. He had many firm friends and former pupils around him in his new post, among them the Grand Duke himself, Cosimo II. But he had also a number of enemies and jealous rivals, both at the Florentine court and at the University of Pisa, where he had taught for a brief time many years before, and where he now held the title of chief mathematician without obligation to teach. It is said that Giovanni de' Medici, an illegitimate son of Cosimo's grandfather, was particularly hostile to Galileo by reason of the latter's unfavorable opinion (later justified by the events) of an engineering project he had undertaken while Galileo was teaching at Pisa. Another old foe was Lodovico delle Colombe, who suspected (probably not without reason) that Galileo had had a hand in the writing of a devastating refutation of his book on the nova of 1604. Several professors at Pisa resented Galileo's privileged position at the university there and his influence over future appointments, and it is natural to suppose that many persons at the court aligned themselves against the newcomer in the usual maneuvers adopted to circumvent rivals for political favor.

Among Galileo's good friends and former pupils was the brilliant nobleman Filippo Salviati, at whose house in Florence and villa near Segni Galileo was a frequent guest. It was probably at Salviati's house, in the latter part of July, that Galileo became engaged in a controversy with Vincenzio di Grazia and Giorgio Coresio, professors at Pisa, on the properties of cold.[16] This led directly to a dispute about the cause of floating and sinking, into which Colombe intruded himself a few days later as champion of Aristotle. An appointment was made for the purpose of settling the argument by means of experiments. Colombe's proposed experiments were quite irrelevant to the original point at issue, and his intended argument was at best an ingenious quibble. Moreover he had the poor judgment to boast openly of his coming victory over Galileo, and to reveal his experiments before the day set for the contest. This was done in public places, and among prominent people, with the twofold effect of forewarning Galileo that the affair threatened to degenerate into a pedantic diversion, and of enabling persons at court to persuade the Grand Duke that his recently appointed mathematician

[16] In presenting the circumstances of the controversy here, I am assuming the correctness of many conclusions set forth in a former paper in which certain evidence is more fully presented, and the conjectural parts are more carefully segregated from the known facts. Cf. *Galileo Gleanings VIII* in Isis, 51, pt. 1, no. 163 (March, 1960), pp. 56ff.

was engaging in public disputes in which nothing was to be gained and possibly a humiliating defeat in the eyes of the public was impending.

It appears that Galileo countered Colombe's actions by appealing to the two judges that had been selected to referee the experiments, and that the judges agreed to disallow the quibble of his opponent, for Colombe failed to appear on the appointed day. Meanwhile, however, the Grand Duke had spoken pointedly though kindly to Galileo about the impropriety of his engaging in oral disputes of this nature. Since Galileo had already issued a new form of the proposition to be debated which would eliminate any quibbling, and a date and place had been set for further argument, he made his appearance but declined to be drawn into discussion, saying rather that he would set forth his views in writing; and during the month of September, 1611, he composed an essay of about fifteen pages. This essay remained unpublished, but has survived nearly intact in manuscript. It bears little resemblance to the *Discourse,* for reasons which will presently appear. Addressed to the Grand Duke in the form of a letter, it began as follows:

"Many are the reasons, Most Serene Lord, for which I have set myself to the writing out at length of the controversy which in past days has led to so much debate by others. Of these, the first and most cogent has been your hint, and your praise of the pen as the unique remedy for purging and separating clear and sequential reasoning from confused and intermittent altercations in which they especially who defend the side of error deny noisily on one occasion that which they had previously affirmed, and on another, pressed by the force of reason, they attempt, with inappropriate distinctions and classifications, cavils, and strained interpretations of words, to slip through one's fingers and escape by their subtleties and twistings about, not hesitating to produce a thousand chimeras and fantastic caprices little understood by themselves and not at all by their listeners. By these the mind is bewildered and confusedly bandied from one phantasm to another, just as, in a dream, one passes from a palace to a ship and thence to a grotto or a beach, and finally, when one awakes and the dream vanishes (and for the most part all memory of it also), one finds that one has been idly sleeping and has passed the hours without profit of any sort.

"The second reason is that I desire that your Highness should become fully and frankly informed of what has taken place in this affair; for the nature of contests being what it is, those who through carelessness are induced to support error will shout loudest and make themselves more heard in public places than those through whom speaks truth, which unmasks itself tranquilly and quietly, though slowly. Hence I can well believe that just as in the squares and temples and other public places, the voices of those who dissent from what I assert have been far more often heard than those of others who agree with me, so likewise at court have they tried to advance their opinion by forestalling me there with their sophisms and cavils; these I hope to disperse and send up in smoke, even though they may have gained the ear and assent of some men prior to a careful reading of this essay of mine.

"In the third place, I have deemed it good not to leave this matter unresolved, for just as at the outset the erroneous side had for nearly everyone the face and appearance of truth, so it might continue to deceive many persons with that same appearance, causing them on some momentous occasions to fall into serious error by taking false axioms for true principles.

"Finally, having been chosen by your Highness as your personal mathematician and philosopher, I cannot permit the malignity, envy, or ignorance (and perhaps all three) of anyone to bear stupidly against your prudence; for this would be to abuse your incomparable benignity. On the contrary, I shall always put down (and with very little trouble) their every impudence, and this I do with the invincible shield of truth, demonstrating that what I have asserted in the past was and is absolutely true, and that to the extent that I have departed from the commonly accepted Peripatetic opinions, this has not come about from my not having read Aristotle, or not having understood as well as they his reasoning, but because I possess stronger demonstrations and more evident experiments than theirs. And in the present dispute, in addition to showing the approach I take to the study of Aristotle, I shall reveal whether I have well understood his meaning in two or three readings only, compared with them, to some of whom the reading of Aristotle fifty times may seem a small matter; and then I shall show whether I have perhaps better investigated the causes of the matters which constitute the subject of the present contest than did Aristotle. . . ."

Here we may pause to note that in this preamble it is evident that Galileo was somewhat uneasy about his reputation at court, as a result of the debate which had become notorious. The "hint" of the Grand Duke was almost certainly a rebuke, mild, perhaps, but nonetheless a rebuke to which Galileo was sensitive. One may believe that his reference to being forestalled at court implies that he had already so far fallen from grace that he was unable to create an opportunity to confront his opponents directly there. The two paragraphs which follow are placed in square brackets, as are other passages which have been cancelled in Galileo's manuscript:

["I have thought it good in this essay of mine not to name any of my adversaries — not because I do not esteem and appreciate them, but because it has reached my ears that they, for whatever reason, do not want their affairs published to the world, and hence I, being unable to hide the things, shall hide the persons, which comes to the same thing. Besides, if (as I expect) it shall happen that I resolve their every argument and irrefutably conclude in favor of my own position, then I think it will not displease them that I have thus kept silent. But if the contrary should happen, it will be up to them to identify themselves in refuting and reprimanding my paralogisms, for which I shall be much indebted, as I glory not in triumphing over my adversaries, but only that truth shall triumph over falsehood.

["I know that your Highness well recalls how, four years ago, I happened in your presence to contradict some engineers, otherwise excellent in their profession, who were devising a method of weaving together a very broad esplanade of timbers. By virtue of the lightness of wood and by a great quantity of wooden tubs made concave and filled with air, on which the esplanade should rest when placed in the water, these men made a great point of the increase in support from the broadness of surface spread over a large body of water, expecting that this would necessarily be capable of sustaining without sinking two or three times as much weight as that which could be precisely and accurately computed for the said planks and beams. Concerning that belief, I said that no great faith should be put in that framework, however spacious, as supporting any more than its separate and disunited parts, or those parts joined in any other framework; and I concluded in general that shape could be neither help nor hindrance to solid bodies with respect to their floating or sinking in water."]

"It was necessary for me some days ago to repeat the same conclusion, and the occasion was a discussion in a circle of gentlemen concerning the four basic qualities.[17] A professor of philosophy said something that is commonplace in the Peripatetic schools, which is that the action of cold was to condense, and he adduced by way of experience the case of ice, affirming that this was nothing but condensed water. Now I, questioning this, remarked that ice should rather be said to be rarefied water; for if it is true that condensation brings about greater heaviness and rarefaction lightness, then since we see that ice is lighter than water, we must also believe that it is less dense. I went on to add that I doubted whether he had not equivocated from 'dense' to 'hard,' and that he meant to say that ice is harder than water, not denser — just as steel is harder, but not denser, than gold. The philosopher immediately denied that ice was less heavy than water and asserted the contrary, to which I replied that this was most evident, since ice floats on water. Thereupon I heard it promptly rejoined that not the lesser heaviness of ice was the cause of its floating on water, being really heavier than water, but rather the cause was its broad and flat shape, which, being unable to cleave the resistance of the water, keeps it on top. Now to this I had two answers: first, I said that not only broad and thin plates of ice remain afloat on water, but pieces of any shape; and I then added that if it were true that ice is really heavier than water, but that a broad and thin plate of it would not submerge, being sustained by the unsuitability of its shape for penetrating the continuous body of the water, one

[17] That is, the qualities of heat, cold, moisture, and dryness, which were made to account for all other properties in the Peripatetic philosophy. At this period "circles" for philosophical discussions were formed in many parts of Italy, and were very popular at Pisa and at Florence.

might test this by driving the ice forcibly under the water and then releasing it; and doubtless one would see it return to float, penetrating and dividing the resistance of the water while going upwards even though that resistance were assisted by the heaviness of the plate which was unable to divide it by descending. At this point, having nothing else to reply [and the gravity of disputation making it necessary for him to stand fixed and immovable upon anything once pronounced], an attempt was made to oppose my demonstration by another experiment. He said that he had observed a thousand times that when the surface of water was struck with the flat of a sword, great resistance to its penetration was felt; whereas a blow with the edge, on the other hand, divided and penetrated it without hindrance. I pointed out his second equivocation by telling him that he now had gone off to another question — that it was one thing to investigate whether different shapes made a difference in the absolute motion or rest of a thing, and quite another to inquire whether it made a difference in its moving more or less swiftly. I added that it is indeed true that broad shapes move slowly while thin ones move swiftly through the same medium; hence the flat of the sword, moved swiftly, meets with greater resistance on striking the water than it would if it were moving with like speed edgewise; nevertheless, a flat shape cannot prevent the sinking of those solid bodies which would go to the bottom in other shapes. And summing up, I concluded my argument with him by this proposition: That a solid body which falls to the bottom in water when reduced to a spherical shape, will also fall there in any other shape, so that in brief, the difference of shape in bodies of the same material does not alter its sinking or not sinking, rising or not rising, in a given medium.

"The philosopher departed, and having thought the matter over and conferred about it with other students of philosophy, he came to find me three days later and said to me that having reasoned on this point with some friends, he had found one who did not fear to contend with me over the question, and who would by reasons and experiments make evident to me the falsity of my proposition. I, ever ready to learn from anyone, replied that I should take it as a favor to converse with this friend of his and reason about the subject.[18]

[18] Galileo does not supply here the actual wording of the question agreed to be debated, or the conditions of the contest. These are preserved, however, in Colombe's later published account of the affair, where the challenge is set forth as follows: "Signor Lodovico delle Colombe being of the opinion that shape affects solid bodies with regard to their descending [or] not descending [and] ascending or not ascending in a given medium, such as water, and in such a manner that for example a solid of spherical figure which would go to the bottom would not do so if altered to some other figure; and I, Galileo Galilei, on the contrary deeming this not to be true, but rather affirming that a solid body which sinks to the bottom in spherical or any other shape will also sink no matter what its shape is, being opposed to Signor Colombe in this particular, am content that we proceed to make experiments of it. And since these experiments might be made in various ways, I am con-

"The game being agreed to by both sides, the place and time were set; but these were not observed by the other party, who not only failed to appear on the appointed day but for many days thereafter. Now this would have mattered little, were it not that this second philosopher, instead of conversing with me and showing me his reasons and experiments, set himself in many public places in the city to show a great multitude of people some little balls and chips of his, first of walnut wood and later of ebony, chanting his triumph and saying that he had me beaten — though he had not so much as spoken with me. Advised of these artifices of his, I comprehended his entire strategy before we ever met; but, the philosophic dispute having thus degenerated into a contentious rivalry, making it impossible to treat the dispute with propriety, I decided that in order to escape from odious contests it would be best to propose in writing a single general argument as the basis and foundation of that which I had asserted, and if this were overthrown, I should admit myself vanquished. And since the experiment produced against me by the adversary was a thin chip of ebony, which, placed on water so that its upper surface is not wetted, does not sink, and a ball of the same material the size of a nut, which goes to the bottom, I, having considered that the cause of this difference proceeds not from shape but from the chip being not wholly wetted, proposed and sent to the adversaries this argument: Every kind of shape, of any size, when wetted, goes to the bottom in water, but if any part of the same shape is not wetted, it will rest without sinking; therefore, not the shape and not the size is the cause of sinking or not sinking, but complete or incomplete wetting."[19]

The next event was described by Colombe as follows:

"On the prescribed day, I appeared at the house of Signor Filippo Salviati, a principal gentleman of our city and as rich in endowments of the mind as in those of fortune, there being present the illustrious and most excellent Signor Don Giovanni Medici, with a host of noble literati, to hear us dispute together. But Signor Galileo could neither be brought to dispute, nor did he wish to perform the experiment with materials of a suitable size, shape, and quantity of material. Rather,

tent that the Very Reverend Signor Canon Nori, as our common friend, shall choose among the experiments that we shall submit, selecting those that may seem to him best suited to reveal the truth, as I also defer to his judgment the decision and the settling of controversies that may arise between the parties in making the said experiments." Colombe added to this, "That the body is to be of the same material and the same weight, but the different shapes are at the choice of Lodovico; and the choice of bodies, which shall be chosen as nearly equal as possible in density [to water?] at the election of Lodovico; and the test shall be made several times, with the same material, but with as many pieces of that material as the number of times the experiment shall be made" (*Opere,* IV, 318-319). The authenticity of Colombe's version is supported by agreement of the opening portion with Galileo's insertion in the second edition of the *Discourse;* see p. 32.

[19] *Opere* IV, 30-35.

he was resolved (and let everyone judge the reason for himself) to publish a treatise of his on this subject, hoping to make others believe by reasoning that which he could not show to the senses; for by altering and adding, and deviating from the agreement and the truth, one may easily draw the true conclusion from false premises and assumptions."[20]

The treatise to which Galileo thus alluded was, of course, the essay of which the opening pages have been set forth above, though when the *Discourse* appeared Colombe mistakenly supposed it to be the writing in question. The essay concluded (after a number of arguments and demonstrations which it is unnecessary to repeat here) as follows:

"Here I expect a terrible rebuke from one of my adversaries, and I can almost hear him shouting in my ears that it is one thing to deal with matters physically, and quite another to do so mathematically, and that geometers should stick to their fantasies and not get entangled in philosophical matters — as if truth could ever be more than one; as if geometry up to our time had prejudiced the acquisition of true philosophy; as if it were impossible to be a geometer as well as a philosopher — and we must infer as a necessary consequence that anyone who knows geometry cannot know physics, and cannot reason about and deal with physical matters physically! Consequences no less foolish than that of a certain physician who, moved by a fit of spleen, said that the great doctor Acquapendente,[21] being a famous anatomist and surgeon, should content himself to remain among his scalpels and ointments, without trying to effect cures by medicine — as if a knowledge of surgery destroyed and opposed a knowledge of medicine. I replied to him that having many times recovered my health through the supreme excellence of Signor Acquapendente, I could depose and certify that he had never given me to drink any compound of cerates, caustics, threads, bandages, probes, and razors, nor had he ever, instead of feeling my pulse, cauterized me or pulled a tooth from my mouth. Rather, as an excellent physician, he purged me with manna, cassia, or rhubarb, and used other remedies suitable to my ailments. Let my adversaries see whether I treat the material in the same terms as Aristotle, and whether he himself does not, where necessary, introduce geometric demonstrations. And then let them have the kindness to desist from their bitter enmity toward geometry — to my astonishment indeed, since I had not thought anyone could be enemy to a total stranger.

"Finally, Aristotle says at the end of his text that one must compare the heaviness of the body with the resistance to division of the medium, because if the power of the heaviness exceeds the resistance of the medium, the body will descend, and if not, it will float. I need not trouble to reply beyond that which has already been said: that it is not resistance to division (which does not exist in air or in water), but

[20] *Ibid.*, 319.

[21] Hieronymous Fabricius of Acquapendente, discoverer of the valves in the veins, teacher of William Harvey, and close friend of Galileo.

rather it is the heaviness of the medium which must be compared with the heaviness of the body, and if the heaviness be greater in the medium, the body will not descend therein, nor can it be entirely submerged, but a part only, since in the space which it occupies in the water there cannot exist a body which weighs less than an equal quantity of water. But if the body be heavier than the water, it will descend to the bottom, where it is more natural for it to rest than a less heavy body. And this is the true, unique, proper, and absolute cause of floating or sinking.

"As for your chip, gentle adversaries, it will float when it is coupled with so much air as to form with it a composite body less heavy than as much water as would fill the space which the said composite occupies in the water; but if you put simple ebony in the water, in accordance with our agreements, it will go to the bottom though you make it thinner than paper.

"Most Serene Lord, I have taken the trouble (as your Highness has seen) to keep alive my true proposition, and along with it many others that follow therefrom, preserving it from the voracity of the falsehood overthrown and slain by me. I know not whether the adversaries will give me credit for the work thus accomplished, or whether they, finding themselves under a strict oath obliged to sustain religiously every decree of Aristotle (perhaps fearing that, if disdained, he might invoke to their destruction a great company of his most invincible heroes), have resolved to choke me off and exterminate me as a profaner of his sacred laws. In this they would imitate the inhabitants of the Isle of Pianto when, angered against Orlando, in recompense for his having liberated so many innocent virgins from the horrible holocaust of the monster, they moved against him, lamenting their strange religion and vainly fearing the wrath of Proteus, terrified of submersion in the vast ocean.[22] And indeed they would have succeeded had not he, impenetrable though naked to their arrows, behaved as does the bear toward small dogs that deafen him with vain and noisy barking. Now I, who am no Orlando, possess nothing impenetrable but the shield of truth; for the rest, naked and unarmed, I take refuge in the protection of your Highness, at whose mere glance must fall any madman who imperiously attempts to mount unreasonable assaults."[23]

III

Galileo was completing his essay toward the end of September, when it chanced that the Grand Duke was visited by two cardinals who enjoyed discussions of philosophical and literary questions. At the same time a professor of philosophy, Flaminio Papazzoni, was present in Florence as a result of his recent appointment to the chair at Pisa left vacant at the end of the previous year by the death of Giulio Libri, a staunch Peripatetic and determined foe of Galileo. Papazzoni's selec-

[22] Ariosto, *Orlando Furioso,* c. xi, 45ff.

[23] *Opere* IV, 49-51.

tion had been made on the recommendation of Galileo, not because of any agreement with his philosophical views, but simply on a basis of his acknowledged ability. The presence of Papazzoni made it possible for Galileo to carry out a project he had long had in mind, which was to debate in the presence of the Medici against a noted professional philosopher who would uphold the views of Aristotle against Galileo's attacks.[24] The result in this instance must have transcended his fondest hopes. At the table of the Grand Duke, one of the cardinals entered the lists on the conventional Aristotelian side, while the other took the side of Galileo. This influential ally was Cardinal Maffeo Barberini, afterward Pope Urban VIII. Several members of the ruling family joined in the argument, among them the Grand Duchess Christina, mother of Cosimo. Various experiments were exhibited and explained; Galileo was able to counter all the philosophical stratagems of his adversaries, and emerged the indisputable victor of the contest.

Immediately after these events, Galileo fell seriously ill. During his recuperation in the winter of 1611, he composed the *Discourse* and discarded the previously completed essay. The difference in tone of the two documents is very marked. Having thoroughly vindicated himself in the eyes of his prince and employer, he did not hesitate to turn his book into a bold and uncompromising blow against the very foundations of Aristotelian physics. Its effectiveness was much enhanced by the colloquial Italian in which it was written.[25] Perhaps of equal importance in this regard was the simplicity and inherent interest of the experiments described, the relevance of which to the decision of the controversy was indisputable. This could not fail to weaken the long-standing tradition under which such disputes were customarily settled by appeal to authority, a tradition that remained the chief obstacle to the development of modern scientific notions.

The *Discourse* appeared in the spring of 1612 and was widely acclaimed. Several replies were published, the first of which was printed anonymously that same summer, its author styling himself merely "The Unknown Academician." This booklet has been attributed to several writers, most authoritatively to Arturo Pannochieschi de' Conti d'Elci, overseer of the University of Pisa, who signed the preface as translator of the work into Italian. Quite possibly, however, the true author was

[24] Galileo had outlined his intention when applying for the title of "philosopher" as well as that of mathematician to the Grand Duke. See *Discoveries,* p. 64.

[25] Galileo gave his reasons for composing this book in Italian, rather than in the scholarly Latin usually used for such treatises, in a celebrated letter to Paolo Gualdo: "I am induced to do this by seeing how young men are sent through the universities at random to be made physicians, philosophers, and so on; thus many of them are committed to professions for which they are unsuited, while other men who would be fitted for these are taken up by family cares and other occupations remote from literature. . . . Now I want them to see that just as nature has given to them, as well as to philosophers, eyes to see her works, so she has also given them brains capable of penetrating and understanding them." (*Opere* XI, 326; *Discoveries,* p. 84.)

Flaminio Papazzoni. The writer speaks as one who had entered the debate only to defend Aristotle and after numerous excesses had been committed by the original adversaries of Galileo, distinguishing himself from them as "one who desires peace." Galileo gave some recognition to this reply when in the second edition of the *Discourse* he defended his technical use of the word *moment* from the criticisms of his anonymous opponent.

At least three other replies were published in the next few months, by Grazia, Colombe, and Coresio, but to these Galileo did not deign to reply directly. Instead, he gave his notes to his distinguished former pupil, Benedetto Castelli, who published a devastating refutation of Grazia and Colombe in 1615. Colombe, who had been present neither at the origin nor at the conclusion of the long controversy, had written as though the *Discourse* were aimed principally at him. Though he was ridiculed for this in Castelli's answer, the notion that Colombe was the ringleader of the opposition continued to prevail until publication of Galileo's discarded essay and his correspondence of the period made possible a reconstruction of the events in some detail. Nevertheless it was to Colombe's attempted quibble that the *Discourse* owed its ingenious and entertaining discussion of the floating under certain conditions of bodies heavier than water.

IV

The translation of Galileo's *Discourse* presented here is a facsimile, except for page numbering, of the very rare original edition described below. Only eight copies are known to exist, of which two are in the United States. The copy employed for the present edition belongs to the library of Manhattan College, to which institution grateful acknowledgment is extended for its use.

The identity of Thomas Salusbury, who translated this and many other works of Galileo into English, remained until quite recently a complete mystery in spite of repeated efforts to clear the matter up. Four years ago the present writer, despairing of success, published the meager results of all previous research on the problem, in the hope that others might be able to add some essential point the importance of which would otherwise remain unrecognized.[26] The hope proved not to be a vain one, though even now the information that has been gained leaves much to be filled in.

The alertness of Mr. Jacob Zeitlin, an antiquarian bookseller who was already thoroughly acquainted with the problem, led early in 1959 to the identification of a dozen letters presently in the Huntington Library as having been written or dictated by the Thomas Salusbury in question.[27] These letters were addressed to the Earl of Huntingdon, by whose guardians Salusbury appears to have been employed for the

[26] *Isis,* 49, n. 155 (March, 1958), pp. 26-33.

[27] *Isis,* 50, n. 162 (December, 1959), pp. 455-458.

purpose of guiding the literary education of the young nobleman and of keeping him and those around him at his country seat informed of political events in London. They bear various dates from July 1663 to April 1665, and in two of these letters (dated in July 1664 and January 1665) the writer alludes to his relations with the printer of the volume containing the *Discourse*. During the period in which these letters were written, Salusbury resided in Highgate, directly north of London. He was married to Susanna Birkenhead (or Birkhened), by whom he had two daughters, the second born in August 1664.

Salusbury's death occurred probably not long before August 1666, when his widow was given the administration of his estate. From various scraps of circumstantial evidence, it seems likely that he was born about 1630; that he was a royalist who spent some years in Italy and France in the decade preceding the return of Charles II to England, and that he became known to Charles during that time; that after the restoration he held for a while the confidence of the king, but fell into some sort of disgrace in 1665, when he was replaced in the service of the Earl of Huntingdon. Salusbury probably put his name as translator to some literary properties that were not his own, but there is no reason to number the *Discourse* among these. It is certain that he was deeply interested in all phases of hydrostatics, hydraulics, and maritime affairs, concerning which he at one time proposed to write a comprehensive treatise, and this fact lends some plausibility to his tentative identification with the "young Mr. Salisbury" to whom Samuel Pepys alludes in his diary.

Salusbury's literary output consisted of the following works:

1. *The Learned Man Defended and Reform'd* . . . by Daniel Bartoli S. J. . . . Englished by Thomas Salusbury. London, R. & W. Leybourn, 1660.

2. *Arnaldo, or, the Injur'd Lover* . . . by . . . Girolamo Brusoni. Made English by T. S. London, Thomas Dring, 1660.

These two books were first entered in the records of the Stationers Company on 29 August 1656 in the copyright of another printer. Both were first printed in June 1660. A curious engraved frontispiece in the first-named displays the arms of Salusbury parted with those of Birkhened. It is probable that this frontispiece was drawn by Salusbury himself, and possibly the face of Ganymede in this allegorical representation is a self-portrait of Salusbury.

The second work is often ascribed to Thomas Sydserf, on the sole authority of an old bookseller's catalogue. It contains a letter of dedication addressed to the young scion of an important Welsh family bearing the name of Salusbury. This letter displays on the part of its writer an intimate familiarity with the pedigrees of the family, though its deferential tone suggests that his own connection therewith was at best rather tenuous.

3. *Mathematical Collections and Translations, the First Tome. . . .* By Thomas Salusbury, Esq. London, W. Leybourn, 1661.

This volume, of which some fifty copies are known today, contains translations by Salusbury of Galileo's *Dialogue* and his *Letter to the Grand Duchess Christina*; Paolo Antonio Foscarini's published letter in defense of the Copernican system on theological grounds; extracts of other banned works of similar tenor; and Benedetto Castelli's work on the measurement of flowing waters. The last-named, which makes up the second part of the first tome, invariably bears an erroneous title page describing it as the second part of the second tome, of which no copy has been seen for more than a century.

4. *Mathematical Collections and Translations, the Second Tome.* London, W. Leybourn, 1665.

Eight copies of this volume are known to survive, containing translations of Galileo's *Two New Sciences, Hydrostatic Balance, Mechanics,* and *Discourse on Bodies in Water,* certain letters of Descartes and Roberval on mechanics, and Archimedes's treatise on floating bodies. Seven of the copies also contain a translation of Tartaglia's work on the raising of sunken vessels (the principal part of the *Ragionamenti* mentioned in note 7, above). A second part of this tome, which contained the translation of a work by Evangelista Torricelli and a biography of Galileo (and perhaps one other work by Salusbury relating to the experimental determination of specific gravities) was almost totally destroyed in the great fire of London shortly after Salusbury's death. A single surviving copy was recorded in 1750 (by Jacques Chaufpié) and again about 1830 (by John Elliott Drinkwater and Stephen Rigaud), but has since disappeared.

For his translation of the *Discourse* there can be little doubt that Salusbury employed the text printed at Bologna in 1655 from the second edition of 1612. This version was edited by Carlo Manolessi in consultation with Vincenzio Viviani. From Salusbury's preface to the second part of the first tome, it is evident that he was in correspondence with Manolessi, and probably it was in this way that he obtained the biographical material which enabled him to attempt the first published *Life of Galileo.* After Salusbury's death, the printer asserted that this *Life* had in fact been written by a Mr. Bargett of Oxford, from letters of Viviani's. The well-preserved correspondence of Viviani, however, shows no trace of any direct communication between him and either Bargett or Salusbury. Another Englishman, Robert Southwell (afterward president of the Royal Society), did arrange with Viviani in 1661 for the publication of such a biography in both English and Latin, but Southwell never carried out this project. Possibly upon Southwell's return to England, Salusbury's proposal to write a life of Galileo came to his attention through the preface to the first tome, and he turned over to Salusbury the material he had obtained from Viviani.

In all editions of the *Discourse* after the first, there are additions which are printed in italic type to distinguish them from Galileo's first text. This tradition was intended to be preserved in Salusbury's translation, but became somewhat obscured by the printer's employment of italics also for certain propositions which in the English version are specificially labeled as definitions, theorems, and corollaries. Departures of Salusbury's text from the original in this and other respects are noted in a list following the text reproduced here, which includes also the principal corrections and emendations of the text and the translation as suggested by the present editor. Omitted from that list are idiosyncrasies of style and language characteristic of Salusbury or of his period, to the extent that these appear unlikely to interfere with a proper understanding of the terms employed.

The use of a facsimile text is more than justified by its value to specialists in several fields and by the extreme rarity of the original. On the other hand, it is certain to create some difficulties for a reader unfamiliar with the science and the vocabulary of Salusbury's period. To the degree that such difficulties can be anticipated, clarifications have been indicated in the list described above. It may be helpful, before reading Salusbury's text, to enter in the margins at the lines indicated the various alterations suggested. Whether or not this is done, it will be important when reading the text to keep in mind certain general remarks set forth below.

First, the word "mass" as employed in this text should always be understood to mean "volume" or "bulk" rather than *mass* in the technical physical sense which it has come to have in our language. Salusbury's word "mass" is a translation of Italian *mole*.

A similar caution is necessary with regard to the word "gravity," which here means simply "heaviness," and has none of the modern physical implications of this word. Likewise, "grave" means merely "heavy," in the sense of "tending downward when set free." It is interesting to see in Salusbury's text the beginnings of a part of our present technical vocabulary, as when (p. 5) he says "equally Grave *in specie*," meaning "of equal specific gravity." As he goes on, he commences to formulate his own English phrases to facilitate reading, so that on p. 37 we find in a single sentence the following: ". . . there is a composition made of Brass and of water, more grave *in specie* [*grave in specie*] than the simple water, but not by vertue of the water infused, as having greater Specifick Gravity [*maggior gravità in specie*] than the other water . . ."

The reader should be warned also that the units of measurement employed by Salusbury have no particular relation to those used by Galileo, and are not always even internally consistent. Words such as "inch," "foot," and "fathom" refer variously to Galileo's *dito* (roughly one inch), *palmo* (roughly four inches), *pied* (roughly eight inches), and *braccio* (roughly 21 inches), with "foot" sometimes employed by Salusbury for any of these except the first.

Next it should be remembered that all the notes and glosses printed in the margins are additions of Salusbury's or the printer's, and have no place in the original.

Finally it should be remarked that the captions "Theorem" and "Corollary" are not to be found in Galileo's text, but are merely the device used by Salusbury to emphasize certain propositions having special importance or logical sequence. Galileo was disinclined to write in the ancient deductive style, even though he stoutly advocated the mathematical treatment of physical matters. A general discussion of his probable reasons for a prejudice against deductive physics would lead us too far afield. In the case of the *Discourse,* we have already seen that Galileo declared his principal interest to have been the stimulation of intelligent lay readers, and doubtless such readers would have been repelled by the rigorous geometric treatment characteristic of Archimedes, though since the time of Newton we have come to take that for granted as the proper manner of expounding physics. The labeling of theorems and corollaries introduced by Salusbury in this work, though it brings the product closer to modern standards, thus does some unintended violence to the style adopted by Galileo in the original.

It is difficult to assess the probable influence of this book upon British scientists of Salusbury's time, which coincided approximately with the first important studies of such eminent scholars as Boyle, Hooke, and Newton. Unlike Galileo's *Dialogue* and his *Mechanics,* which circulated in manuscript English translations almost from the time of their first publications, the *Discourse* is not known to have existed in any translation except Salusbury's. That the rare second tome of his *Mathematical Collections* was avidly sought after is known from a letter of John Collins to Dr. John Pell shortly after the fire, in which he said that copies were fetching fifty shillings, "an unconscionable price," and that the demand far exceeded the supply.[28] Undoubtedly the few surviving copies circulated among scholars both at Oxford and Cambridge, and the unique complete copy was in the collection of William Jones, a close friend of Newton's. But the *Discourse,* though it almost certainly had a seminal value at the time, was not cited directly by any British writer on hydrostatics.

[28] Stephen Rigaud, *Correspondence of British Scientific Men of the Seventeenth Century,* Oxford, 1841, II, 463.

A DISCOURSE

PRESENTED

TO THE MOST SERENE

Don Cosimo II.

GREAT DUKE

OF

TUSCANY,

CONCERNING

The *NATATION* of BODIES Vpon,

And *SUBMERSION* In,

THE

WATER.

By GALILEUS GALILEI: Philosopher and
Mathematician unto His most Serene Highnesse.

Englished from the Second Edition of the ITALIAN,
compared with the Manuscript Copies, and reduced
into PROPOSITIONS:
By *THOMAS SALUSBURY*, Esq;

LONDON:
Printed by WILLIAM LEYBOURN:
M DC LXIII.

A DISCOVRSE
Presented to the Most Serene Don Cosimo II. Great Duke of *TUSCANY*: CONCERNING *The Natation of BODIES Upon, or Submersion In, the WATER.*

COnsidering (Most Serene Prince) that the publishing this present Treatise, of so different an Argument from that which many expect, and which according to the intentions I proposed in my * Astronomicall *Adviso*, I should before this time have put forth, might peradventure make some thinke, either that I had wholly relinquished my farther imployment about the new Celestiall Observations, or that, at least, I handled them very remissely; I have judged fit to render an account, aswell of my deferring that, as of my writing, and publishing this treatise.

* His Nuncio Siderio.

As to the first, the last discoveries of *Saturn* to be tricorporeall, and of the mutations of Figure in *Venus*, like to those that are seen in the Moon, together with the Consequents depending thereupon, have not so much occasioned the demur, as the investigation of the times of the Conversions of each of the Four Medicean Planets about *Jupiter*, which I lighted upon in *April* the year past, 1611, at my being in *Rome*; where, in the end, I assertained my selfe, that the first and neerest to *Jupiter*, moved about 8 *gr.* & 29 *m.* of its Sphere in an houre, makeing its whole revolution in one naturall day, and 18 hours, and almost an halfe. The second moves in its Orbe 14 *gr.* 13 *min.* or very neer, in an hour, and its compleat conversion is consummate in 3 dayes, 13 hours, and one third, or thereabouts. The third passeth in an hour, 2 *gr.* 6 *min.* little more or less of its Circle, and measures it all in 7 dayes, 4 hours, or very neer. The fourth, and more remote than the rest, goes in one houre, 0 *gr* 54 *min.* and almost an halfe of its Sphere, and finisheth it all in 16 dayes, and very neer 18 hours. But because the excessive velocity of their returns or restitutions, requires a most scrupulous precisenesse to calculate their places, in times past

 and

and future, especially if the time be for many Moneths or Years; I am therefore forced, with other Observations, and more exact than the former, and in times more remote from one another, to correct the Tables of such Motions, and limit them even to the shortest moment: for such exactnesse my first Observations suffice not; not only in regard of the short intervals of Time, but because I had not as then found out a way to measure the distances between the said Planets by any Instrument: I Observed such Intervals with simple relation to the Diameter of the Body of *Jupiter*; taken, as we have said, by the eye, the which, though they admit not errors of above a Minute, yet they suffice not for the determination of the exact greatness of the Spheres of those Stars. But now that I have hit upon a way of taking such measures without failing, scarce in a very few *Seconds*, I will continue the observation to the very occultation of *JUPITER*, which shall serve to bring us to the perfect knowledge of the Motions, and Magnitudes of the Orbes of the said Planets, together also with some other consequences thence arising. I adde to these things the observation of some obscure Spots, which are discovered in the Solar Body, which changing, position in that, propounds to our consideration a great argument either that the Sun revolves in it selfe, or that perhaps other Starts, in like manner as *Venus* and *Mercury*, revolve about it, invisible in other times, by reason of their small digressions, lesse than that of *Mercury*, and only visible when they interpose between the Sun and our eye, or else hint the truth of both this and that; the certainty of which things ought not to be contemned, nor omitted.

The Authors Observations of the Solar Spots.

Continuall observation hath at last assured me that these Spots are matters contiguous to the Body of the Sun, there continually produced in great number, and afterwards dissolved, some in a shorter, some in a longer time, and to be by the Conversion or Revolution of the Sun in it selfe, which in a Lunar Moneth, or thereabouts, finisheth its Period, caried about in a Circle, an accident great of it selfe, and greater for its Consequences.

The occasion inducing the Author to write this Treatise.

As to the other particular in the next place * Many causes have moved me to write the present Tract, the subject whereof, is the Dispute which I held some dayes since, with some learned men of this City, about which, as your Highnesse knows, have followed many Discourses: The principall of which Causes hath been the Intimation of your Highnesse, having commended to me Writing, as a singular means to make true known from false, reall from apparent Reasons, farr better than by Disputing vocally, where the one or the other, or very often both the Disputants, through too

great

greate heate, or exalting of the voyce, either are not understood, or else being transported by ostentation of not yeilding to one another, farr from the first Proposition, with the novelty, of the various Proposals, confound both themselves and their Auditors.

Moreover, it seemed to me convenient to informe your Highnesse of all the sequell, concerning the Controversie of which I treat, as it hath been advertised often already by others: and because the Doctrine which I follow, in the discussion of the point in hand, is different from that of *Aristotle*; and interferes with his Principles, I have considered that against the Authority of that most famous Man, which amongst many makes all suspected that comes not from the Schooles of the Peripateticks, its farr better to give ones Reasons by the Pen than by word of mouth, and therfore I resolved to write the present discourse: in which yet I hope to demonstrate that it was not out of capritiousnesse, or for that I had not read or understood *Aristotle*, that I sometimes swerve from his opinion, but because severall Reasons perswade me to it, and the same *Aristotle* hath tought me to fix my judgment on that which is grounded upon Reason, and not on the bare Authority of the Master; and it is most certaine according to the sentence of *Alcinoos*, that philosophating should be free. Nor is the resolution of our Question in my judgment without some benefit to the Universall, forasmuch as treating whether the figure of Solids operates, or not, in their going, or not going to the bottome in Water, in occurrences of building Bridges or other Fabricks on the Water, which happen commonly in affairs of grand import, it may be of great availe to know the truth.

Aristotle prefers Reason to the Authority of an Author.

The benefit of this Argument.

I say therfore, that being the last Summer in company with certain Learned men, it was said in the argumentation; That Condensation was the propriety of Cold, and there was alledged for instance, the example of Ice: now I at that time said, that, in my judgment, the Ice should be rather Water rarified than condensed, and my reason was, because Condensation begets diminution of Mass, and augmentation of gravity, and Rarifaction causeth greater Lightness, and augmentarion of Masse: and Water in freezing, encreaseth in Masse, and the Ice made thereby is lighter than the Water on which it swimmeth.

Condensation the Propriety of Cold, according to the Peripateticks.

Ice rather water rarified, than condensed, and why:

What I say, is manifest, because, the medium subtracting from the whole Gravity of Sollids the weight of such another Masse of the said Medium; as Archimedes *proves in his * First Booke* De Insidentibus Humido; *when ever the Masse of the said Solid encreaseth by Distraction, the more shall the* Medium *detract from its entire Gravity; and lesse, when by Compression it shall be condensed and reduced to a lesse Masse.*

In lib: 1. of Natation of Bodies Prop. 7.

Figure operates not in the Natation of Sollids.

It was answered me,tha that proceeded not from the greater Levity, but from the Figure, large and flat, which not being able to penetrate the Resistance of the Water,is the cause that it submergeth not. I replied,that any piece of Ice, of whatsoever Figure, swims upon the Water, a manifest signe, that its being never so flat and broad, hath not any part in its floating: and added, that it was a manifest proofe hereof to see a piece of Ice of very broad Figure being thrust to the botome of the Water, suddenly return to flote atoppe, which had it been more grave, and had its swimming proceeded from its Forme, unable to penetrate the Resistance of the *Medium*, that would be altogether impossible; I concluded therefore,that the Figure was in sort a Cause of the Natation or Submersion of Bodies, but the greater or lesse Gravity in respect of the Water: and therefore all Bodyes heavier than it of what Figure soever they be, indifferently go to the bottome,and the lighter,though of any figure, float indifferently on the top: and I suppose that those which hold otherwise, were induced to that beliefe, by seeing how that diversity of Formes or Figures, greatly altereth the Velosity, and Tardity of Motion; so that Bodies of Figure broad and thin, descend far more leasurely into the Water, than those of a more compacted Figure, though both made of the same Matter: by which some might be induced to believe that the Dilatation of the Figure might reduce it to such amplenesse that it should not only retard but wholly impede and take away the Motion, which I hold to be false. Upon this Conclusion, in many dayes discourse, was spoken much, and many things, and divers Experiments produced, of which your Highnesse heard, and saw some, and in this discourse shall have all that which hath been produced against my Assertion, and what hath been suggested to my thoughts on this matter, and for confirmation of my Conclusion: which if it shall suffice to remove that (as I esteem hitherto false) Opinion, I shall thinke I have not unprofitably spent my paynes and time. and although that come not to passe, yet ought I to promise another benefit to my selfe, namely, of attaining the knowledge of the truth, by hearing my Fallacyes confuted, and true demonstrations produced by those of the contrary opinion.

And to proceed with the greatest plainness and perspicuity that I can possible, it is, I conceive, necessary, first of all to declare what is the true, intrinsecall, and totall Cause, of the ascending of some Sollid Bodyes in the Water, and therein floating; or on the contrary, of their sinking and so much the rather in asmuch as I cannot satisfie my selfe in that which *Aristotle* hath left written on this Subject.

The cause of the Natation & sub-

I say then the Cause why some Sollid Bodyes descend to the Bottom

Bottom of Water, is the excesse of their Gravity, above the Gravity of the Water; and on the contrary, the excels of the Waters Gravity above the Gravity of those, is the Cause that others do not descend, rather that they rise from the Bottom, and ascend to the Surface. This was subtilly demonstrated by *Archimedes* in his Book Of the NATATION of BODIES: Conferred afterwards by a very grave Author, but, if I erre not invisibly, as below for defence of him, I shall endeavour to prove.

mersion of Solids in the Water.

I, with a different Method, and by other meanes, will endeavour to demonstrate the same, reducing the Causes of such Effects to more intrinsecall and immediate Principles, in which also are discovered the Causes of some admirable and almost incredible Accidents, as that would be, that a very little quantity of Water, should be able, with its small weight, to raise and sustain a Solid Body, an hundred or a thousand times heavier than it.

And because demonstrative Order so requires, I shall define certain Termes, and afterwards explain some Propositions, of which, as of things true and obvious, I may make use of to my present purpose.

DEFINITION I.

I then call equally Grave in specie, *those Matters of which equall Masses weigh equally.*

As if for example, two Balls, one of Wax, and the other of some Wood of equall Masse, were also equall in Weight, we say, that such Wood, and the Wax are *in specie* equally grave.

DEFINITION II.

But equally grave in Absolute Gravity, we call two Sollids, weighing equally, though of Mass they be unequall.

As for example, a Mass of Lead, and another of Wood, that weigh each ten pounds, I call equall in Absolute Gravity, though the Mass of the Wood be much greater then that of the Lead.

And, consequently, less Grave in specie.

DEFINITION III.

I call a Matter more Grave in specie *than another, of which a Mass, equall to a Mass of the other, shall weigh more.*

And

And so I say, that Lead is more grave *in specie* than Tinn, because if you take of them two equall Masses, that of the Lead weigheth more.

DEFINITION IV.

But I call that Body more grave absolutely than this, if that weigh more than this, without any respect had to the Masses.

And thus a great piece of Wood is said to weigh more than a little lump of Lead, though the Lead be *in specie* more heavy than the Wood. And the same is to be understood of the less grave *in specie*, and the less grave absolutely.

These Termes defined, I take from the Mechanicks two Principles : the first is, that

AXIOME. I.

Weights absolutely equall, moved with equall Velocity, are of equall Force and Moment in their operations.

DEFINITION V.

Moment, amongst Mechanicians, signifieth that Vertue, that Force, or that Efficacy, with which the Mover moves, and the Moveable resists.

Which Vertue dependes not only on the simple Gravity, but on the Velocity of the Motion, and on the diverse Inclinations of the Spaces along which the Motion is made : For a descending Weight makes a greater Impetus *in a Space much declining, than in one less declining ; and in summe, what ever is the occasion of such Vertue, it ever retaines the name of* Moment ; *nor in my Judgement, is this sence new in our Idiome, for, if I mistake not, I think we often say ; This is a weighty businesse, but the other is of small moment : and we consider lighter matters and let pass those of Moment ; a Metaphor, I suppose, taken from the Mechanicks.*

As for example, two weights equall in absolute Gravity, being put into a Ballance of equall Arms, they stand in *Equilibrium*, neither one going down, nor the other up : because the equality of the Distances of both, from the Centre on which the Ballance is supported, and about which it moves, causeth that those weights, the said Ballance moving, shall in the same Time move equall Spaces, that is, shall move with equall Velocity, so that there is no reason for which this Weight ſhould deſcend more than that, or that more than this; and therefore they make an *Equilibrium*, and their Moments continue of ſemblable and equall Vertue.

The ſecond Principle is; That

AXIOME II.

The Moment and Force of the Gravity, is encreaſed by the Velocity of the Motion.

So that Weights abſolutely equall, but conjoyned with Velocity unequall, are of Force, Moment and Vertue unequall: and the more potent, the more ſwift, according to the proportion of the Velocity of the one, to the Velocity of the other. Of this we have a very pertinent example in the Balance or Stiliard of unequall Arms, at which Weights abſolutely equall being ſuſpended, they do not weigh down, and gravitate equally, but that which is at a greater diſtance from the Centre, about which the Beam moves, deſcends, raiſing the other, and the Motion of this which aſcends is ſlow, and the other ſwift: and ſuch is the Force and Vertue, which from the Velocity of the Mover, is conferred on the Moveable, which receives it, that it can exquiſitely compenſate, as much more Weight added to the other ſlower Moveable: ſo that if of the Arms of the Balance, one were ten times as long as the other, whereupon in the Beames moving about the Centre, the end of that would go ten times as far as the end of this, a Weight ſuſpended at the greater diſtance, may ſuſtain and poyſe another ten times more grave abſolutely than it: and that becauſe the Stiliard moving, the leſſer Weight ſhall move ten times faſter than the bigger. It ought alwayes therefore to be underſtood, that Motions are according to the ſame Inclinations, namely, that if one of the Moveables move perpendicularly to the Horizon, then the other makes its Motion by the like Perpendicular; and if the Motion of one were to be made Horizontally; that then the other is made along the ſame Horizontall plain: and in ſumme, alwayes both in like Inclinations. This proportion between the Gravity and Velocity is found in all Mechanicall Inſtruments: and is conſidered by *Ariſtotle*, as a Principle in his *Mechanicall Queſtions*; whereupon we alſo may take it for a true Aſſumption, That

AXIOME III.

Weights abſolutely unequall, do alternately counterpoyſe and become of equall Moments, as oft as their Gravities, with contrary proportion, anſwer to the Velocity of their Motions.

That

That is to ſay,that by how much the one is leſs grave than the other, by ſo much is it in a conſtitution of moving more ſwiftly than that.

Having prefatically explicated theſe things, we may begin to enquire, what Bodyes thoſe are which totally ſubmerge in Water, and go to the Bottom, and which thoſe that by conſtraint float on the top, ſo that being thruſt by violence under Water, they return to ſwim, with one part of their Maſs viſible above the Surface of the Water : and this we will do by conſidering the reſpective operation of the ſaid Solids, and of Water : Which operation followes the Submerſion and ſinking; and this it is, That in the Submerſion that the Solid maketh, being depreſſed downwards by its proper Gravity, it comes to drive away the water from the place where it ſucceſſively ſubenters, and the water repulſed riſeth and aſcends above its firſt levell, to which Aſcent on the other ſide it, as being a grave Body of its own nature, reſiſts : And becauſe the deſcending Solid more and more immerging, greater and greater quantity of Water aſcends, till the whole Sollid be ſubmerged; its neceſſary to compare the Moments of the Reſiſtance of the water to Aſcenſion, with the Moments of the preſſive Gravity of the Solid : And if the Moments of the Reſiſtance of the water, ſhall equalize the Moments of the Solid, before its totall Immerſion; in this caſe doubtleſs there ſhall be made an *Equilibrium*, nor ſhall the Body ſink any farther. But if the Moment of the Solid, ſhall alwayes exceed the Moments wherewith the repulſed water ſucceſſively makes Reſiſtance, that Solid ſhall not only wholly ſubmerge under water, but ſhall deſcend to the Bottom. But if, laſtly, in the inſtant of totall Submerſion, the equality ſhall be made between the Moments of the prement Solid, and the reſiſting Water; then ſhall reſt, enſue, and the ſaid Solid ſhall be able to reſt indifferently, in whatſoever part of the water. By this time is manifeſt the neceſſity of comparing the Gravity of the water, and of the Solid; and this compariſon might at firſt ſight ſeem ſufficient to conclude and determine which are the Solids that float a-top, and which thoſe that ſink to the Bottom in the water, aſſerting that thoſe ſhall float which are leſſe grave *in ſpecie* than the water, and thoſe ſubmerge, which are *in ſpecie* more grave. For it ſeems in appearance, that the Sollid in ſinking continually, raiſeth ſo much Water in Maſs, as anſwers to the parts of its own Bulk ſubmerged : whereupon it is impoſſible, that a Solid leſs grave *in ſpecie*, than water,ſhould wholly ſink, as being unable to raiſe a weight greater than its own, and ſuch would a Maſs of water equall to its own Maſs be. And likewiſe it ſeems neceſſary, that the graver Solids do go to the Bottom, as being of a Force more than ſufficient for the raiſing a Maſſe of water, equall to its own, though inferiour in weight. Nevertheleſs the buſineſs ſucceeds otherwiſe : and though

How the ſubmerſion of Solids in the Water, is effected.

What Solids ſhall float on the Water.

What Solids ſhall ſinke to the botome.

What Solids ſhall reſt in all places of the Water.

The Gravitie of the Water and Solid muſt be compared in all Problems of Natation of Bodies.

though the Conclusions are true, yet are the Causes thus assigned deficient, nor is it true, that the Solid in submerging, raiseth and repulseth Masses of Water, equall to the parts of it self submerged; but the Water repulsed, is alwayes less than the parts of the Solid submerged : and so much the more by how much the Vessell in which the Water is contained is narrower : in such manner that it hinders not, but that a Solid may submerge all under Water, without raising so much Water in Mass, as would equall the tenth or twentieth part of its own Bulk : like as on the contrary, a very small quantity of Water, may raise a very great Solid Mass, though such Solid should weigh absolutely a hundred times as much, or more, than the said Water, if so be that the Matter of that same Solid be *in specie* less grave than the Water. And thus a great Beam, as suppose of a 1000 weight, may be raised and born afloat by Water, which weighs not 50 : and this happens when the Moment of the Water is compensated by the Velocity of its Motion.

The water repulsed is ever less than the parts of the Sollid submerged.

A small quantity of water, may float a very great Solid Mass.

But because such things, propounded thus in abstract, are somewhat difficult to be comprehended, it would be good to demonstrate them by particular examples; and for facility of demonstration, we will suppose the Vessels in which we are to put the Water, and place the Solids, to be inviron'd and included with sides erected perpendicular to the Plane of the Horizon, and the Solid that is to be put into such vessell to be either a streight Cylinder, or else an upright Prisme

The which proposed and declared, I proceed to demonstrate the truth of what hath been hinted, forming the ensuing Theoreme.

THEOREME I.

The Mass of the Water which ascends in the submerging of a Solid, Prisme or Cylinder, or that abaseth in taking it out, is less than the Mass of the said Solid, so depressed or advanced : and hath to it the same proportion, that the Surface of the Water circumfusing the Solid, hath to the same circumfused Surface, together with the Base of the Solid.

The Proportion of the water raised to the Solid submerged.

LEt the Vessell be A B C D, and in it the Water raised up to the Levell E F G, before the Solid Prisme H I K be therein immerged; but after that it is depressed under Water, let the Water be raised as high as the Levell L M, the Solid H I K shall then be all under Water, and the Mass of the elevated Water shall be L G, which is less than the

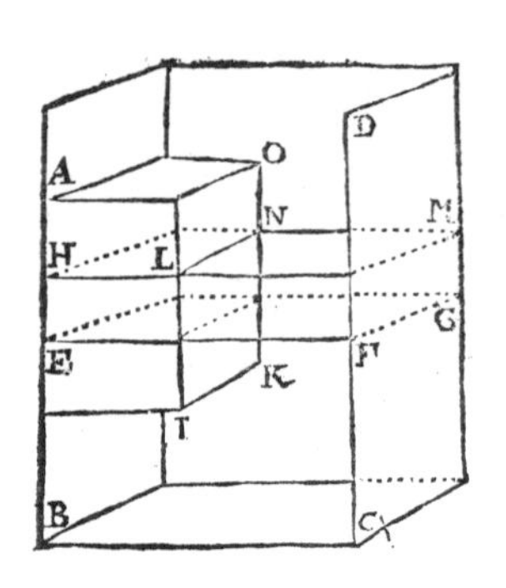

Maſſe of the Solid depreſſed, namely of HIK, being equall to the only part EIK, which is contained under the firſt Levell EFG. Which is manifeſt, becauſe if the Solid HIK be taken out, the Water IG ſhall return into the place occupied by the Maſs EIK, where it was continuate before the ſubmerſion of the Priſme. And the Maſs LG being equall to the Maſs EK: adde thereto the Maſs EN, and it ſhall be the whole Maſs EM, compoſed of the parts of the Priſme EN, and of the Water NF, equall to the whole Solid HIK: And, therefore, the Maſs LG ſhall have the ſame proportion to EM, as to the Maſs HIK: But the Maſs LG hath the ſame proportion to the Maſs EM, as the Surface LM hath to the Surface MH: Therefore it is manifeſt, that the Maſs of Water repulſed LG, is in proportion to the Maſs of the Solid ſubmerged HIK; as the Surface LM, namely, that of the Water ambient about the Sollid, to the whole Surfaoe HM, compounded of the ſaid ambient water, and the Baſe of the Priſme HN. But if we ſuppoſe the firſt Levell of the Water the according to the Surface HM, and the Priſme allready ſubmerged HIK; and after to be taken out and raiſed to EAO, and the Water to be faln from the firſt Levell HLM as low as EFG; It is manifeſt, that the Priſme EAO being the ſame with HIK, its ſuperiour part HO, ſhall be equall to the inferiour EIK: and remove the common part EN, and, conſequently, the Maſs of the Water LG is equall to the Maſs HO; and, therefore, leſs than the Solid, which is without the Water, namely, the whole Priſme EAO, to which likewiſe, the ſaid Maſs of Water abated LG, hath the ſame proportion, that the Surface of the Waters circumfuſed LM hath to the ſame circumfuſed Surface, together with the Baſe of the Priſme AO: which hath the ſame demonſtration with the former caſe above.

And from hence is inferred, that the Maſs of the Water, that riſeth in the immerſion of the Solid, or that ebbeth in elevating it, is not equall to all the Maſs of the Solid, which is ſubmerged or elevated, but to that part only, which in the immerſion is under the firſt Levell of the Water, and in the elevation remaines above the firſt Levell: Which is that which was to be demonſtrated. We will now purſue the things that remain.

And firſt we will demonſtrate that,

THEO-

THEOREME II.

When in one of the above ſaid Veſſels, of what ever breadth, whether wide or narrow, there is placed ſuch a Priſme or Cylinder, inviron'd with Water, if we elevate that Solid perpendicularly, the Water circumfuſed ſhall abate, and the Abatement of the Water, ſhall have the ſame proportion to the Elevation of the Priſme, as one of the Baſes of the Priſme, hath to the Surface of the Water Circumfuſed.

The proportion of the water abated, to the Solid raiſed.

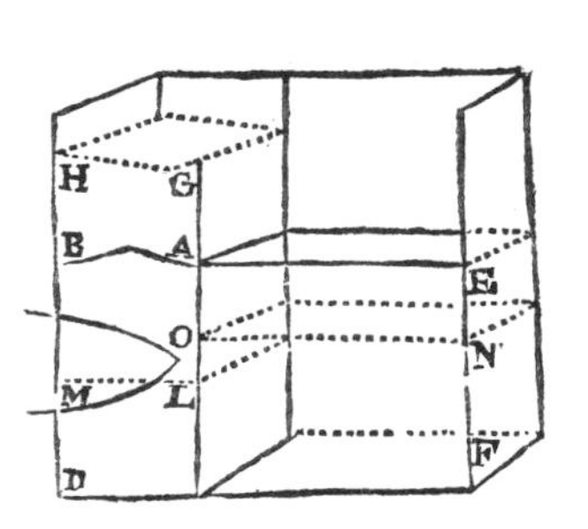

IMagine in the Veſſell, as is aforeſaid, the Priſme A C D B to be placed, and in the reſt of the Space the Water to be diffuſed as far as the Levell E A : and raiſing the Solid, let it be transferred to G M, and let the Water be abaſed from E A to N O : I ſay, that the deſcent of the Water, meaſured by the Line A O, hath the ſame proportion to the riſe of the Priſme, meaſured by the Line G A, as the Baſe of the Solid G H hath to the Surface of the Water N O. The which is manifeſt : becauſe the Maſs of the Solid G A B H, raiſed above the firſt Levell E A B, is equall to the Maſs of Water that is abaſed E N O A. Therefore, E N O A and G A B H are two equall Priſmes; for of equall Priſmes, the Baſes anſwer contrarily to their heights : Therefore, as the Altitude A O is to the Altitude A G, ſo is the Superficies or Baſe G H to the Surface of the Water N O. If therefore, for example, a Pillar were erected in a waſte Pond full of Water, or elſe in a Well, capable of little more then the Maſs of the ſaid Pillar, in elevating the ſaid Pillar, and taking it out of the Water, according as it riſeth, the Water that invirons it will gradually abate, and the abaſement of the Water at the inſtant of lifting out the Pillar, ſhall have the ſame proportion, that the thickneſs of the Pillar hath to the exceſs of the breadth of the ſaid Pond or Well, above the thickneſs of the ſaid Pillar : ſo that if the breadth of the Well were an eighth part larger than the thickneſs of the Pillar, and the breadth of the Pond twenty five times as great as the ſaid thickneſs, in the Pillars aſcending one foot, the water in the Well ſhall deſcend ſeven foot, and that in the Pond only $\frac{1}{25}$ of a foot.

Why a Solid leſs grave *in ſpecie* than water, ſtayeth not under water, in very ſmall depths.

This Demonſtrated, it will not be difficult to ſhew the true cauſe, how it comes to paſs, that,

THEOREME III.

A Prisme or regular Cylinder, of a substance specifically less grave than Water, if it should be totally submerged in Water, stayes not underneath, but riseth, though the Water circumfused be very little, and in absolute Gravity, never so much inferiour to the Gravity of the said Prisme.

Let then the Prisme A E F B, be put into the Vessell C D F B, the same being less grave *in specie* than the Water : and let the Water infused rise to the height of the Prisme : I say, that the Prisme left at liberty, it shall rise, being born up by the Water circumfused C D E A. For the Water C E being specifically more grave than the Solid A F, the absolute weight of the water C E, shall have greater proportion to the absolute weight of the Prisme A F, than the Mass C E hath to the Mass A F (in regard the Mass hath the same proportion to the Mass, that the weight absolute hath to the weight absolute, in case the Masses are of the same Gravity *in specie.*) But the Mass C E is to the Mass A F, as the Surface of the water A C, is to the Superficies, or Base of the Prisme A B ; which is the same proportion as the ascent of the Prisme when it riseth, hath to the descent of the water circumfused C E.

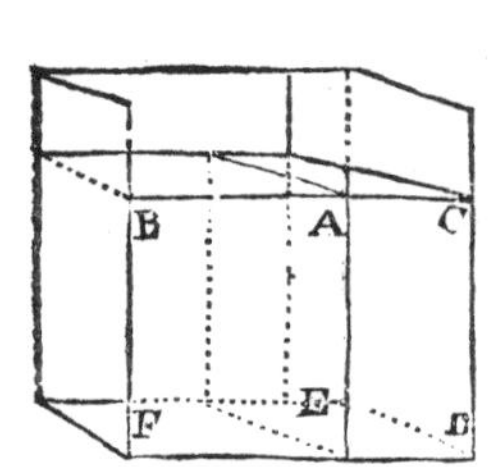

Therefore, the absolute Gravity of the water C E, hath greater proportion to the absolute Gravity of the Prisme A F ; than the Ascent of the Prisme A F , hath to the descent of the said water C E. The Moment, therefore, compounded of the absolute Gravity of the water C E, and of the Velocity of its descent, whilst it forceably repulseth and raiseth the Solid A F, is greater than the Moment compounded of the absolute Gravity of the Prisme A F, and of the Tardity of its ascent, with which Moment it contrasts and resists the repulse and violence done it by the Moment of the water: Therefore, the Prisme shall be raised.

The Proportion according to which the Submersion & Natation of Solids is made.

It followes, now, that we proceed forward to demonstrate more particularly, how much such Solids shall be inferiour in Gravity to the water elevated ; namely, what part of them shall rest submerged, and what shall be visible above the Surface of the water : but first it is necessary to demonstrate the subsequent Lemma.

LEMM

LEMMA I.

The absolute Gravities of Solids, have a proportion compounded of the proportions of their specificall Gravities, and of their Masses.

The absolute Gravity of Solids, are in a proportion compounded of their Specifick Gravities, and of their Masses.

LEt A and B be two Solids. I say, that the Absolute Gravity of A, hath to the Absolute Gravity of B, a proportion compounded of the proportions of the specificall Gravity of A, to the Specificall Gravity of B, and of the Mass A to the Mass B. Let the Line D have the same proportion to E, that the specifick Gravity of A, hath to the specifick Gravity of B; and let E be to F, as the Mass A to the Mass B: It is manifest, that the proportion of D to F, is compounded of the proportions D and E; and E and F. It is requisite,

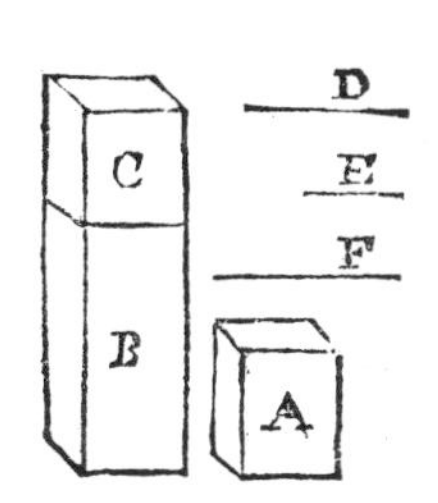

therefore, to demonstrate, that as D is to F, so the absolute Gravity of A, is to the absolute Gravity of B. Take the Solid C, equall in Mass to the Solid A, and of the same Gravity *in specie* with the Solid B. Because, therefore, A and C are equall in Mass, the absolute Gravity of A, shall have to the absolute Gravity of C, the same proportion, as the specificall Gravity of A, hath to the specificall Gravity of C, or of B, which is the same *in specie*; that is, as D is to E. And, because, C and B are of the same Gravity *in specie*, it shall be, that as the absolute weight of C, is to the absolute weight of B, so the Mass C, or the Mass A, is to the Mass B; that is, as the Line E to the Line F. As therefore, the absolute Gravity of A, is to the absolute Gravity of C, so is the Line D to the Line E: and, as the absolute Gravity of C, is to the absolute Gravity of B, so is the Line E to the Line F: Therefore, by Equality of proportion, the absolute Gravity of A, is to the absolute Gravity of B, as the Line D to the Line F: which was to be demonstrated. I proceed now to demonstrate, how that,

THEO-

THEOREME IV.

The proportion of water requisite to make a Solid swim.

If a Solid, Cylinder, or Prisme, lesse grave specifically than the Water, being put into a Vessel, as above, of whatsoever greatnesse, and the Water, be afterwards infused, the Solid shall rest in the bottom, unraised, till the Water arrive to that part of the Altitude, of the said Prisme, to which its whole Altitude hath the same proportion, that the Specificall Gravity of the Water, hath to the Specificall Gravity of the said Solid: but infusing more Water, the Solid shall ascend.

LEt the Vessell be M L G N of any bigness, and let there be placed in it the Solid Prisme D F G E, less grave *in specie* than the water; and look what proportion the Specificall Gravity of the water, hath to that of the Prisme, such let the Altitude D F, have to the Altitude F B. I say, that infusing water to the Altitude F B, the Solid D G shall not float, but shall stand in *Equilibrium*, so, that that every little quantity of water, that is infused, shall raise it. Let the water, therefore, be infused to the Levell A B C; and; because the Specifick Gravity of the Solid D G, is to the Specifick Gravity of the water, as the altitude B F is to the altitude F D; that is, as the Mass B G to the Mass G D; as the proportion of the Mass B G is to the Mass G D, as the proportion of the Mass G D is to the Mass A F, they compose the Proportion of the Mass B G to the Mass A F. Therefore, the Mass B G is to the Mass A F; in a proportion compounded of the proportions of the Specifick Gravity of the Solid G D, to the Specifick Gravity of the water, and of the Mass G D to the Mass A F: But the same proportions of the Specifick Gravity of G D, to the Specifick Gravity of the water, and of the Mass G D to the Mass A F, do also by the precedent *Lemma*, compound the proportion of the absolute Gravity of the Solid D G, to the absolute Gravity of the Mass of the water A F: Therefore, as the Mass B G is to the Mass A F, so is the Absolute Gravity of the Solid D G, to the Absolute Gravity of the Mass of the water A F. But as the Mass B G is to the Mass A F; so is the Base of the Prisme D E, to the Surface of the water AB; and so is the descent of the water A B, to the Elevation of the Prisme D G; Therefore, the descent of the water

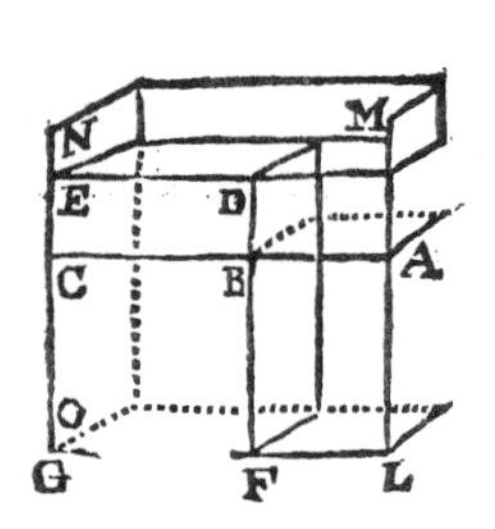

water is to the elevation of the Prisme, as the absolute Gravity of the Prisme, is to the absolute Gravity of the water: Therefore, the Moment resulting from the absolute Gravity of the water A F, and the Velocity of the Motion of declination, with which Moment it forceth the Prisme D G, to rise and ascend, is equall to the Moment that results from the absolute Gravity of the Prisme D G, and from the Velocity of the Motion, wherewith being raised, it would ascend: with which Moment it resists its being raised: because, therefore, such Moments are equall, there shall be an *Equilibrium* between the water and the Solid. And, it is manifest, that putting a little more water unto the other A F, it will increase the Gravity and Moment, whereupon the Prisme D G, shall be overcome, and elevated till that the only part B F remaines submerged. Which is that that was to be demonstrated.

COROLLARY I.

By what hath been demonstrated, it is manifest, that Solids less grave in specie *than the water, submerge only so far, that as much water in Mass, as is the part of the Solid submerged, doth weigh absolutely as much as the whole Solid.*

How far Solids less grave *in specie* than water, do submerge.

For, it being supposed, that the Specificall Gravity of the water is to the Specificall Gravity of the Prisme D G, as the Altitude D F, is to the Altitude F B; that is, as the Solid D G is to the Solid B G; we might easily demonstrate, that as much water in Mass as is equall to the Solid B G, doth weigh absolutely as much as the whole Solid D G; For, by the *Lemma* foregoing, the Absolute Gravity of a Mass of water, equall to the Mass B G, hath to the Absolute Gravity of the Prisme D G, a proportion compounded of the proportions, of the Mass B G to the Mass G D, and of the Specifick Gravity of the water, to the Specifick Gravity of the Prisme: But the Gravity *in specie* of the water, to the Gravity *in specie* of the Prisme, is supposed to be as the Mass G D to the Mass G B. Therefore, the Absolute Gravity of a Mass of water, equall to the Mass B G, is to the Absolute Gravity of the Solid D G, in a proportion compounded of the proportions, of the Mass B G to the Mass G D, and of the Mass D G to the Mass G B; which is a proportion of equalitie. The Absolute Gravity, therefore, of a Mass of Water equall to the part of the Mass of the Prisme B G, is equall to the Absolute Gravity of the whole Solid D G.

COROL-

COROLLARY II.

A Rule to equilibrate Solids in the water.

It followes, moreover, that a Solid less grave than the water, being put into a Vessell of any imaginable greatness, and water being circumfused about it to such a height, that as much water in Mass, as is the part of the Solid submerged, do weigh absolutely as much as the whole Solid; it shall by that water be justly sustained, be the circumfused Water in quantity greater or lesser.

For, if the Cylinder or Prisme M, less grave than the water, *v. gra.* in Subsequiteriall proportion, shall be put into the capacious Vessell A B C D, and the water raised about it, to three quarters of its height, namely, to its Levell A D: it shall be sustained and exactly poysed in *Equilibrium.* The same will happen; if the Vessell E N S F were very small, so, that between the Vessell and the Solid M, there were but a very narrow space, and only capable of so much water, as the hundredth part of the Mass M, by which it should be likewise raised and erected, as before it had been elevated to three fourths of the height of the Solid: which to many at the first sight, may seem a notable Paradox, and beget a conceit, that the Demonstration of these effects, were sophisticall and fallacious: but, for those who so repute it, the Experiment is a means that may fully satisfie them. But he that shall but comprehend of what Importance Velocity of Motion is, and how it exactly compensates the defect and want of Gravity, will cease to wonder, in considering that at the elevation of the Solid M, the great Mass of water A B C D abateth very little, but the little Mass of water E N S F decreaseth very much, and in an instant, as the Solid M before did rise, howbeit for a very short space: Whereupon the Moment, compounded of the small Absolute Gravity of the water E N S F, and of its great Velocity in ebbing, equalizeth the Force and and Moment, that results from the composition of the immense Gravity of the water A B C D, with its great slownesse of ebbing; since that in the Elevation of the Sollid M, the abasement of the lesser water E S, is performed just so much more swiftly than the great Mass of water A C, as this is more in Mass than that which we thus demonstrate.

The proportion according to which water riseth and falls in different Vessels at the Immersion and Elevation of Solids.

In the rising of the Solid M, its elevation hath the same proportion to the circumfused water E N S F, that the Surface of the said water, hath to the Superficies or Base of the said Solid M; which Base hath the same proportion to the Surface of the water A D, that the abasement

ment or ebbing of the water A C, hath to the rise or elevation of the said Solid M. Therefore, by Perturbation of proportion, in the ascent of the said Solid M, the abasement of the water A B C D, to the abasement of the water E N S F, hath the same proportion, that the Surface of the water E F, hath to the Surface of the water A D; that is, that the whole Mass of the water E N S F, hath to the whole Mass A B C D, being equally high: It is manifest, therefore, that in the expulsion and elevation of the Solid M, the water E N S F shall exceed in Velocity of Motion the water A B C D, asmuch as it on the other side is exceeded by that in quantity: whereupon their Moments in such operations, are mutually equall.

And, for ampler confirmation, and clearer explication of this, let us consider the present Figure, (which if I be not deceived, may serve to detect the errors of some Practick Mechanitians, who upon a false foundation some times attempt impossible enterprizes,) in which, unto the large Vessell E I D F, the narrow Funnell or Pipe I C A B is continued, and suppose water infused into them, unto the Levell L G H, which water shall rest in this position, not without admiration in some, who cannot conceive how it can be, that the heavie charge of the great Mass of water G D, pressing downwards, should not elevate and repulse the little quantity of the other, contained in the Funnell or Pipe C L, by which the descent of it is resisted and hindered: But such wonder shall cease, if we begin to suppose the water G D to be abased only to Q D, and shall afterwards consider, what the water C L hath done, which to give place to the other, which is descended from the Levell G H, to the Levell Q O, shall of necessity have ascended in the same time, from the Levell L unto A B. And the ascent L B, shall be so much greater than the descent G Q, by how much the breadth of the Vessell G D, is greater than that of the Funnell I C; which, in summe, is as much as the water G D, is more than the water L C: but in regard that the Moment of the Velocity of the Motion, in one Moveable, compensates that of the Gravity of another, what wonder is it, if the swift ascent of the lesser Water C L, shall resist the slow descent of the greater G D?

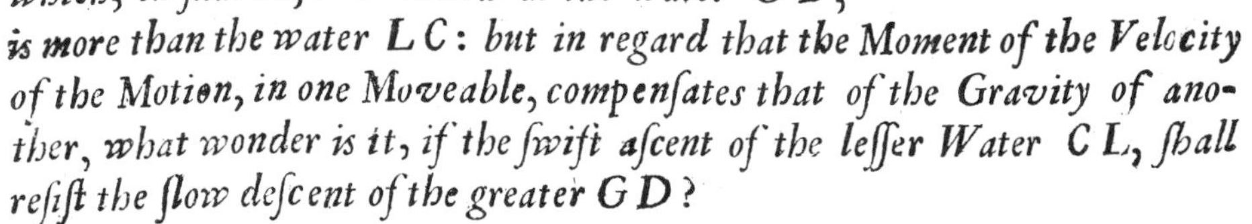

The same, therefore, happens in this operation, as in rhe Stilliard, in which a weight of two pounds counterpoyseth an other of 200, as often as that shall move in the same time, a space 100 times greater than this: which falleth out when one Arme of the Beam is an hundred times as long as the other. Let the erroneous opinion of those therefore cease, who hold that a Ship is better, and easier born up in a great abundance of water, then in a lesser quantity, (*this was believed by* Aristotle *in his Problems, Sect.* 23, *Probl.* 2.) it being on the contrary true, that its possible, that a Ship may as well float in ten Tun of water, as in an Ocean.

A Ship flotes as well in ten Tun of water as in an Ocean.

But following our matter, I say, that by what hath been hitherto demonstrated, we may understand how, that

A Solid specifically graver than the water, cannot be born up by any quantity of it.

COROLLARY III.

One of the above named Solids, when more grave in specie *than the water, can never be sustained, by any whatever quantity of it.*

For having seen how that the Moment wherewith such a Solid, as grave *in specie* as the water, contrasts with the Moment of any Mass of water whatsoever, is able to retain it, even to its totall Submersion, without its ever ascending; it remaineth, manifest, that the water is far less able to raise it up, when it exceeds the same *in specie*: so, that though you infuse water till its totall Submersion, it shall still stay at the Bottome, and with such Gravity, and Resistance to Elevation, as is the excess of its Absolute Gravity, above the Absolute Gravity of a Mass equall to it, made of water, or of a Matter *in specie* equally grave with the water: and, though you should moreover adde never so much water above the Levell of that which equalizeth the Altitude of the Solid, it shall not, for all that, encrease the Pression, or Gravitation, of the parts circumfused about the said Solid, by which greater pression, it might come to be repulsed; because, the Resistance is not made, but only by those parts of the water, which at the Motion of the said Solid do also move, and these are those only, which are comprehended by the two Superficies equidistant to the Horizon, and their parallels, that comprehend the Altitude of the Solid immerged in the water.

I conceive, I have by this time sufficiently declared and opened the way to the contemplation of the true, intrinsecall and proper Causes of diverse Motions, and of the Rest of many Solid Bodies in diverse *Mediums*, and particularly in the water, shewing how all in effect, depend on the mutuall excesses of the Gravity of the Moveables and of the *Mediums*: and, that which did highly import, removing the Objection, which peradventure would have begotten much doubting, and scruple in some, about the verity of my Conclusion, namely, how that notwithstanding, that the excess of the Gravity of the water, above the Gravity of the Solid, demitted into it, be the cause of its floating and rising from the Bottom to the Surface, yet a quantity of water, that weighs not ten pounds, can raise a Solid

Solid that weighs above 100 pounds: in that we have demonstrated, That it sufficeth, that such difference be found between the Specificall Gravities of the *Mediums* and Moveables, let the particular and absolute Gravities be what they will: insomuch, that a Solid, provided that it be Specifically less grave than the water, although its absolute weight were 1000 pounds, yet may it be born up and elevated by ten pounds of water, and less: and on the contrary, another Solid, so that it be Specifically more grave than the water, though in absolute Gravity it were not above a pound, yet all the water in the Sea, cannot raise it from the Bottom, or float it. This sufficeth me, for my present occasion, to have, by the above declared Examples, discovered and demonstrated, without extending such matters farther, and, as I might have done, into a long Treatise: yea, but that there was a necessity of resolving the above proposed doubt, I should have contented my self with that only, which is demonstrated by *Archimedes*, in his first Book *De Insidentibus humido*: where in generall termes he infers and confirms the same Conclusions, namely, that Solids (*a*) less grave than water, swim or float upon it, the (*b*) more grave go to the Bottom, and the (*c*) equally grave rest indifferently in all places, yea, though they should be wholly under water.

Of Natation

(a) *Lib.1. Prop.4.*
(b) *Id. Lib. 1. Prop. 3.*
(c) *Id. Lib. 1. Prop. 3.*

But, because that this Doctrine of *Archimedes*, perused, transcribed and examined by *Signor Francesco Buonamico*, in his *fifth Book of Motion, Chap. 29*, and afterwards by him confuted, might by the Authority of so renowned, and famous a Philosopher, be rendered dubious, and suspected of falsity; I have judged it necessary to defend it, if I am able so to do, and to clear *Archimedes*, from those censures, with which he appeareth to be charged. *Buonamico* rejecteth the Doctrine of *Archimedes*, first, as not consentaneous with the Opinion of *Aristotle*, adding, that it was a strange thing to him, that the Water should exceed the Earth in Gravity, seeing on the contrary, that the Gravity of water, increaseth, by means of the participation of Earth. And he subjoyns presently after, that he was not satisfied with the Reasons of *Archimedes*, as not being able with that Doctrine, to assign the cause whence it comes, that a Boat and a Vessell, which otherwise, floats above the water, doth sink to the Bottom, if once it be filled with water; that by reason of the equality of Gravity, between the water within it, and the other water without, it should stay a top; but yet, neverthelesse, we see it to go to the Bottom.

The Authors defence of *Archimedes* his Doctrine, against the oppositions of *Buonamico*.

His first Objection against the Doctrine of *Archimedes*.

His Second Objection.

His third Objection.

He farther addes, that *Aristotle* had clearly confuted the Ancients, who said, that light Bodies moved upwards, driven by the impulse of the more grave Ambient: which if it were so, it should seem of necessity to follow, that all naturall Bodies are by nature heavy, and

His fourth Objection.

The *Antients* denyed *Absolute* Levity.

and none light : For that the ſame would befall the Fire and Air, if put in the Bottom of the water. And, howbeit, *Ariſtotle* grants a Pulſion in the Elements, by which the Earth is reduced into a Sphericall Figure, yet nevertheleſs, in his judgement; it is not ſuch that it can remove grave Bodies from their naturall places, but rather, that it ſend them toward the Centre, to which (as he ſomewhat obſcurely continues to ſay,) the water principally moves, if it in the interim meet not with ſomething that reſiſts it, and, by its Gravity, thruſts it out of its place : in which caſe, if it cannot directly, yet at leaſt as well as it can, it tends to the Centre : but it happens, that light Bodies by ſuch Impulſion, do all aſcend upward : but this properly they have by nature, as alſo, that other of ſwimming. He concludes, laſtly, that he concurs with *Archimedes* in his Concluſions; but not in the Cauſes, which he would referre to the facile and difficult Separation of the *Medium*, and to the predominance of the Elements, ſo that when the Moveable ſuperates the power of the *Medium*; as for example, Lead doth the Continuity of water, it ſhall move thorow it, elſe not.

The cauſes of Natation & Submerſion, according to the Peripateticks.

This is all that I have been able to collect, as produced againſt *Archimedes* by *Signor Buonamico* : who hath not well obſerved the Principles and Suppoſitions of *Archimedes*; which yet muſt be falſe, if the Doctrine be falſe, which depends upon them; but is contented to alledge therein ſome Inconveniences, and ſome Repugnances to the Doctrine and Opinion of *Ariſtotle*. In anſwer to which Objections, I ſay, firſt, That the being of *Archimedes* Doctrine, ſimply different from rhe Doctrine of *Ariſtotle*, ought not to move any to ſuſpect it, there being no cauſe, why the Authority of this ſhould be preferred to the Authority of the other : but, becauſe, where the decrees of Nature are indifferently expoſed to the intellectuall eyes of each, the Authority of the one and the other, loſeth all anthenticalneſs of Perſwaſion, the abſolute power reſiding in Reaſon; therefore I paſs to that which he alledgeth in the ſecond place, as an abſurd conſequent of the Doctrine of *Archimedes*, namely, That water ſhould be more grave than Earth. But I really find not, that ever *Archimedes* ſaid ſuch a thing, or that it can be rationally deduced from his Concluſions : and if that were manifeſt unto me, I verily believe, I ſhould renounce his Doctrine, as moſt erroneous. Perhaps this Deduction of *Buonamico*, is founded upon that which he citeth of the Veſſel, which ſwims as long as its voyd of water, but once full it ſinks to the Bottom, and underſtanding it of a Veſſel of Earth, he infers againſt *Archimedes* thus: Thou ſayſt that the Solids which ſwim, are leſs grave than water: this Veſſell ſwimmeth: therefore, this Veſſell is leſſe grave than water. If this be the Illation. I eaſily anſwer, granting that this Veſſell is leſſe grave than water, and denying the other conſequence,

The Authors anſwer to the firſt Objection.

The Authors anſwer to the ſecond Objection.

namely,

namely, that Earth is less Grave than Water. The Vessel that swims occupieth in the water, not only a place equall to the Mass of the Earth, of which it is formed; but equall to the Earth and to the Air together, contained in its concavity. And, if such a Mass compounded of Earth and Air, shall be less grave than such another quantity of water, it shall swim, and shall accord with the Doctrine of *Archimedes*; but if, again, removing the Air, the Vessell shall be filled with water, so that the Solid put in the water, be nothing but Earth, nor occupieth other place, than that which is only possest by Earth, it shall then go to the Bottom, by reason that the Earth is heavier than the water: and this corresponds well with the meaning of *Archimedes*. See the same effect illustrated, with such another Experiment, In pressing a Viall Glass to the Bottom of the water, when it is full of Air, it will meet with great resistance, because it is not the Glass alone, that is pressed under water, but together with the Glass a great Mass of Air, and such, that if you should take as much water, as the Mass of the Glass, and of the Air contained in it, you would have a weight much greater than that of the Viall, and of its Air: and, therefore, it will not submerge without great violence: but if we demit only the Glass into the water, which shall be when you shall fill the Glass with water, then shall the Glass descend to the Bottom; as superiour in Gravity to the water.

Returning, therefore, to our first purpose; I say, that Earth is more grave than water, and that therefore, a Solid of Earth goeth to the bottom of it; but one may possibly make a composition of Earth and Air, which shall be less grave than a like Mass of Water; and this shall swim: and yet both this and the other experiment shall very well accord with the Doctrine of *Archimedes*. But because that in my judgment it hath nothing of difficulty in it, I will not positively affirme that *Signor Buonamico*, would by such a discourse object unto *Archimedes* the absurdity of inferring by his doctrine, that Earth was less grave than Water, though I know not how to conceive what other accident he could have induced thence.

Perhaps such a Probleme (in my judgement false) was read by *Signor Buonamico* in some other Author, by whom peradventure it was attributed as a singular propertie, of some particular Water, and so comes now to be used with a double errour in confutation of *Archimedes*, since he saith no such thing, nor by him that did say it was it meant of the common Element of Water.

The Authors answer to the third Objection.

The third difficulty in the doctrine of *Archimedes* was, that he could not render a reason whence it arose, that a piece of Wood, and a Vessell of Wood, which otherwise floats, goeth to the bottom, if filled with Water. *Signor Buonamico* hath supposed that a Vessell of Wood, and of Wood that by nature swims, as before is said, goes

goes to the bottom, if it be filled with water; of which he in the following Chapter, which is the 30 of the fifth Book copiously discourseth: but I (speaking alwayes without diminution of his singular Learning) dare in defence of *Archimedes* deny this experiment, being certain that a piece of Wood which by its nature sinks not in Water, shall not sinke though it be turned and converted into the forme of any Vessell whatsoever, and then filled with Water: and he that would readily see the Experiment in some other tractable Matter, and that is easily reduced into several Figures, may take pure Wax, and making it first into a Ball or other solid Figure, let him adde to it so much Lead as shall just carry it to the bottome, so that being a graine less it could not be able to sinke it, and making it afterwards into the forme of a Dish, and filling it with Water, he shall finde that without the said Lead it shall not sinke, and that with the Lead it shall descend with much slowness: & in short he shall satisfie himself, that the Water included makes no alteration. I say not all this while, but that its possible of Wood to make Barkes, which being filled with water, sinke; but that proceeds not through its Gravity, encreased by the Water, but rather from the Nailes and other Iron Workes, so that it no longer hath a Body less grave than Water, but one mixt of Iron and Wood, more grave than a like Masse of Water. Therefore let *Signor Buonamico* desist from desiring a reason of an effect, that is not in nature: yea if the sinking of the Woodden Vessell when its full of Water, may call in question the Doctrine of *Archimedes*, which he would not have you to follow, is on the contrary consonant and agreeable to the Doctrine of the Peripateticks, since it aptly assignes a reason why such a Vessell must, when its full of Water, descend to the bottom; converting the Argument the other way, we may with safety say that the Doctrine of *Archimedes* is true, since it aptly agreeth with true experiments, and question the other, whose Deductions are fastened upon erroneouss Conclusions. As for the other point hinted in this same Instance, where it seemes that *Benonamico* understands the same not only of a piece of wood, shaped in the forme of a Vessell, but also of massie Wood, which filled, *scilicet*, as I believe, he would say, soaked and steeped in Water, goes finally to the bottom that happens in some porose Woods, which, while their Porosity is replenished with Air, or other Matter less grave than Water, are Masses specificially less grave than the said Water, like as is that Viall of Glass whilest it is full of Air: but when, such light Matter departing, there succeedeth Water into the same Porosities and Cavities, there results a compound of Water and Glass more grave than a like Mass of Water: but the excess of its Gravity consists in the Matter of the Glass, and not in the Water, which cannot be graver than it self: so that which remaines of the Wood, the Air of its Cavi-

tyes

ties departing, if it shall be more grave *in specie* than Water, fil but its Porosities with Water, and you shal have a Compost of Water and of Wood more grave than Water, but not by vertue of the Water received into and imbibed by the Porosities, but of that Matter of the Wood which remains when the Air is departed : and being such it shall, according to the Doctrine of *Archimedes*, goe to the bottom, like as before, according to the same Doctrine it did swim.

As to that finally which presents it self in the fourth place, namely, that the *Ancients* have been heretofore confuted by *Aristotle*, who denying Positive and Absolute Levity, and truely esteeming all Bodies to be grave, said, that that which moved upward was driven by the circumambient Air, and therefore that also the Doctrine of *Archimedes* , as an adherent to such an Opinion was convicted and confuted : I answer first, that *Signor Buonamico* in my judgement hath imposed upon *Archimedes*, and deduced from his words more than ever he intended by them, or may from his Propositions be collected, in regard that *Archimedes* neither denies, nor admitteth Positi ve Levity, nor doth he so much as mention it: so that much less ought *Buonamico* to inferre, that he hath denyed that it might be the Cause and Principle of the Ascension of Fire, and other Light Bodies : having but only demonstrated, that Solid Bodies more grave than Water descend in it, according to the excess of their Gravity above the Gravity of that, he demonstrates likewise, how the less grave ascend in the same Water, accordng to its excess of Graty, above the Gravity of them. So that the most that can be gathered from the Demonstration of *Archimedes* is, that like as the excess of the Gravity of the Moveable above the Gravity of the Water, is the Cause that it descends therein, so the excess of the Gravity of the water above that of the Moveable, is a sufficient Cause why it descends not, but rather betakes it self to swim : not enquiring whether of moving upwards there is, or is not any other Cause contrary to Gravity : nor doth *Archimedes* discourse less properly than if one should say : If the South Winde shall assault the Barke with greater *Impetus* than is the violence with which the Streame of the River carries it towards the South, the motion of it shall be towards the North : but if the *Impetus* of the Water shall overcome that of the Winde, its motion shall be towards the South. The discourse is excellent and would be unworthily contradicted by such as should oppose it, saying: Thou mis-alledgest as Cause of the motion of the Bark towards the South, the *Impetus* of the Stream of the Water above that of the South Winde ; mis-alledgest I say, for it is the Force of the North Winde opposite to the South, that is able to drive the Bark towards the South. Such an Objection would be superfluous, because he which alledgeth for Cause of the Motion the stream of the Water, denies not but

The Authors answer to the fourth Objection.

Of Natation, Lib. 1. Prop. 7.

Of Natation, Lib. 1. Prop. 4.

but that the Winde opposite to the South may do the same, but only affirmeth that the force of the Water prevailing over the South Wind, the Bark shall move towards the South: and saith no more than is true. And just thus when *Archimedes* saith, that the Gravity of the Water prevailing over that by which the moveable descends to the Bottom, such moveable shall be raised from the Bottom to the Surface alledgeth a very true Cause of such an Accident, nor doth he affirm or deny that there is, or is not, a vertue contrary to Gravity, called by some Levity, that hath also a power of moving some Matters upwards. Let therefore the Weapons of *Signor Buonamico* be directed against *Plato*, and other *Ancients*, who totally denying *Levity*, and taking all Bodies to be grave, say that the Motion upwards is made, not from an intrinsecal Principle of the Moveable, but only by the Impulse of the *Medium*; and let *Archimedes* and his Doctrine escape him, since he hath given him no Cause of quarelling with him. But if this Apologie, produced in defence of *Archimedes*, should seem to some insufficient to free him from the Objections and Arguments, produced by *Aristotle* against *Plato*, and the other *Ancients*, as if they did also fight against *Archimedes*, alledging the Impulse of the Water as the Cause of the swimming of some Bodies less grave than it, I would not question, but that I should be able to maintaine the Doctrine of *Plato* and those others to be most true, who absolutely deny Levity, and affirm no other Intrinsecal Principle of Motion to be in Elementary Bodies save only that towards the Centre of the Earth, nor no other Cause of moving upwards, speaking of that which hath the resemblance of natural Motion, but only the repulse of the *Medium*, fluid, and exceeding the Gravity of the Moveable: and as to the Reasons of *Aristotle* on the contrary, I believe that I could be able fully to answer them, and I would assay to do it, if it were absolutely necessary to the present Matter, or were it not too long a Digression for this short Treatise. I will only say, that if there were in some of our Ellementary Bodies an Intrinsecall Principle and Naturall Inclination to shun the Centre of the Earth, and to move towards the Concave of the Moon, such Bodies, without doubt, would more swiftly ascend through those *Mediums* that least oppose the Velocity of the Moveable, and these are the more tenuous and subtle; as is, for example, the Air in comparison of the Water, we daily proving that we can with farre more expeditious Velocity move a Hand or a Board to and again in one than in the other: neverthelesse, we never could finde any Body, that did not ascend much more swiftly in the water than in the Air. Yea of Bodies which we see continually to ascend in the Water, there is none that having arrived to the confines of the Air, do not wholly lose their Motion; even the Air it self, which rising with great Celerity through the Water, being once come to its Region it loseth all

Plato denyeth Positive Levity.

The Authors defence of the doctrine of *Plato* and the *Ancients*, who absolutely deny Levity.

According to *Plato* there is no Principle of the Motion of descent in Naturall Bodies, save that to the Centre.

No cause of the motion of Ascent, save the Impulse of the *Medium*, exceeding the Moveable in Gravitie.

Bodies ascend much swifter in the Water, than in the Air.

All Bodies ascending through Water, lose their Motion, comming to the confines of the Air.

Im-

And, howbeit, Experience ſhewes, that the Bodies, ſucceſſively leſs grave, do moſt expeditiouſly aſcend in water, it cannot be doubted, but that the Ignean Exhalations do aſcend more ſwiftly through the water, than doth the Air: which Air is ſeen by Experience to aſcend more ſwiftly through the Water, than the Fiery Exhalations through the Air: Therefore, we muſt of neceſſity conclude, that the ſaid Exhalations do much more expeditiouſly aſcend through the Water, than through the Air; and that, conſequently, they are moved by the Impulſe of the Ambient *Medium*, and not by an intrinſick Principle that is in them, of avoiding the Centre of the Earth; to which other grave Bodies tend.

The lighter Bodies aſcend more ſwiftly through Water. Fiery Exhalations aſcend thorow the Water more ſwiftly than doth the Air; & the Air aſcends more ſwiftly thorow the Water, than Fire thorow the Air.

To that which for a finall concluſion, *Signor Buonamico* produceth of going about to reduce the deſcending or not deſcending, to the eaſie and uneaſie Diviſion of the *Medium*, and to the predominancy of the Elements: I anſwer, as to the firſt part, that that cannot in any manner be admitted as a Cauſe, being that in none of the Fluid *Mediums*, as the Air, the Water, and other Liquids, there is any Reſiſtance againſt Diviſion, but all by every the leaſt Force, are divided and penetrated, as I will anon demonſtrate: ſo, that of ſuch Reſiſtance of Diviſion there can be no Act, ſince it ſelf is not in being. As to the other part, I ſay, that the predominancy of the Elements in Moveables, is to be conſidered, as far as to the exceſſe or defect of Gravity, in relation to the *Medium*: for in that Action, the Elements operate not, but only, ſo far as they are grave or light: therefore, to ſay that the Wood of the Firre ſinks not, becauſe Air predominateth in it, is no more than to ſay, becauſe it is leſs grave than the Water. Yea, even the immediate Cauſe, is its being leſs grave than the Water: and it being under the predominancy of the Air, is the Cauſe of its leſs Gravity: Therefore, he that alledgeth the predominancy of the Element for a Cauſe, brings the Cauſe of the Cauſe, and not the neereſt and immediate Cauſe. Now, who knows not that the true Cauſe is the immediate, and not the mediate? Moreover, he that alledgeth Gravity, brings a Cauſe moſt perſpicuous to Sence: The cauſe we may very eaſily aſſertain our ſelves; whether Ebony, for example, and Firre, be more or leſs grave than water: but whether Earth or Air predominates in them, who ſhall make that manifeſt? Certainly, no Experiment can better do it than to obſerve whether they ſwim or ſink. So, that he who knows, not whether ſuch a Solid ſwims, unleſs when he knows that Air predominates in it, knows not whether it ſwim, unleſs he ſees it ſwim, for then he knows that it ſwims, when he knows that it is Air that predominates, but knows not that Air hath the predominance, unleſs he ſees it ſwim: therefore, he knows not if it ſwims, till ſuch time as he hath ſeen it ſwim.

The Authors confutation of the Peripateticks Cauſes of Natation & Submerſion.

Water & other fluids void of Reſiſtance againſt Diviſion.

The predominancy of Elements in Moveables to be conſidered only in relation to their exceſs or defect of Gravity in reference to the Medium.

The immediate Cauſe of Natation is that the Moveable is leſs grave than the Water.

The Peripateticks alledge for the reaſon of Natation the Cauſe of the Cauſe.

Gravity a Cauſe moſt perſpicuous to ſence.

Let us not then despise those Hints, though very dark, which Reason, after some contemplation, offereth to our Intelligence, and lets be content to be taught by *Archimedes*, that then any Body shall submerge in water, when it shall be specifically more grave than it, and that if it shall be less grave, it shall of necessity swim, and that it will rest indifferently in any place under water, if its Gravity be perfectly like to that of the water.

Lib. 1. of Natation Prop. 7. Id. Lib. 1. Prop. 4.

These things explained and proved, I come to consider that which offers it self, touching what the Diversity of figure given unto the said Moveable hath to do with these Motions and Rests; and proceed to affirme, that,

Id. Lib. 1. Prop. 3.

THEOREME V.

The diversity of Figures given to this or that Solid, cannot any way be a Cause of its absolute Sinking or Swimming.

Diversity of Figure no Cause of its absolute Natation or Submersion.

SO that if a Solid being formed, for example, into a Sphericall Figure, doth sink or swim in the water, I say, that being formed into any other Fi ure, the same figure in the same water, shall sink or swim: nor can such its Motion by the Expansion or by other mutation of Figure, be impeded or taken away.

The Expansion of the Figure may indeed retard its Velocity, as well of ascent as descent, and more and more according as the said Figure is reduced to a greater breadth and thinness: but that it may be reduced to such a form as that that same matter be wholly hindred from moving in the same water, that I hold to be impossible. In this I have met with great contradictors, who producing some Experiments, and in perticular a thin Board of Ebony, and a Ball of the same Wood, and shewing how the Ball in Water descended to the bottom, and the Board being put lightly upon the Water submerged not, but rested; have held, and with the Authority of *Aristotle*, confirmed themselves in their Opinions, that the Cause of that Rest was the breadth of the Figure, u able by its small weight to pierce and penetrate the Resistance of the Waters Crassitude, which Resistance is readily overcome by the other Sphericall Figure.

The Expansion of Figure, retards the Velocity of the ascent or descent of the Moveable in the water; but doth not deprive it of all Motion.

This is the Principal point in the present Question, in which I perswade my self to be on the right side.

Therefore, beginning to investigate with the examination of exquisite Experiments that really the Figure doth not a jot alter the descent or Ascent of the same Solids, and having already demonstrated that the greater or less Gravity of the Solid in relation to the Gravity of the *Medium* is the cause of Descent or Ascent: when ever we would

would make proof of that, which about this Effect the diversity of Figure worketh, its necessary to make the Experiment with Matter wherein variety of Gravities hath no place. For making use of Matters which may be different in their Specifical Gravities, and meeting with varieties of effects of Ascending and Descending, we shall alwayes be left unsatisfied whether that diversity derive it self really from the sole Figure, or else from the divers Gravity also. We may remedy this by takeing one only Matter, that is tractable and easily reduceable into every sort of Figure. Moreover, it wil be an excellent expedient to take a kinde of Matter, exactly alike in Gravity unto the Water: for that Matter, as far as pertaines to the Gravity, is indifferent either to Ascend or Descend; so that we may presently observe any the least difference that derives it self from the diversity of Figure.

An Experiment in Wax, that proveth Figure to have no Operation in Natation & Submersion.

Now to do this, Wax is most apt, which, besides its incapacity of receiveing any sensible alteration from its imbibing of Water, is ductile or pliant, and the same piece is easily reduceable into all Figures: and being *in specie* a very inconsiderable matter inferiour in Gravity to the Water, by mixing therewith a little of the fileings of Lead it is reduced to a Gravity exactly equall to that of the Water.

This Matter prepared, and, for example, a Ball being made thereof as bigge as an Orange or biger, and that made so grave as to sink to the bottom, but so lightly, that takeing thence one only Grain of Lead, it returnes to the top, and being added, it submergeth to the bottom, let the same Wax afterwards be made into a very broad and thin Flake or Cake; and then, returning to make the same Experiment, you shall see that it being put to the bottom, it shall, with the Grain of Lead rest below, and that Grain deducted, it shall ascend to the very Surface, and added again it shall dive to the bottom. And this same effect shall happen alwaies in all sort of Figures, as wel regular as irregular: nor shall you ever finde any that will swim without the removall of the Grain of Lead, or sinke to the bottom unless it be added: and, in short, about the going or not going to the Bottom, you shall discover no diversity, although, indeed, you shall about the quick and slow descent: for the more expatiated and distended Figures move more slowly aswel in the diveing to the bottom as in the rising to the top; and the other more contracted and compact Figures, more speedily. Now I know not what may be expected from the diversity of Figures, if the most contrary to one another operate not so much as doth a very small Grain of Lead, added or removed.

An objection against the Experiment in Wax.

Me thinkes I hear some of the Adversaries to raise a doubt upon my produced Experiment. And first, that they offer to my consideration, that the Figure, as a Figure simply, and disjunct from the Matter workes not any effect, but requires to be conjoyned with the Matter;

and, furthermore, not with every Matter, but with those only, wherewith it may be able ro execute the desired operation. Like as we see it verified by Experience, that the Acute and sharp Angle is more apt to cut, than the Obtuse; yet alwaies provided, that both the one and the other, be joyned with a Matter apt to cut, as for example, with Steel. Therefore, a Knife with a fine and sharp edge, cuts Bread or Wood with much ease, which it will not do, if the edge be blunt and thick: but he that will instead of Steel, take Wax, and mould it into a Knife, undoubtedly shall never know the effects of sharp and blunt edges: because neither of them will cut, the Wax being unable by reason of its flexibility, to overcome the hardness of the Wood and Bread. And, therefore, applying the like discourse to our purpose, they say, that the difference of Figure will shew different effects, touching Natation and Submersion, but not conjoyned with any kind of Matter, but only with those Matters which, by their Gravity, are apt to resist the Velocity of the water, whence he that would elect for the Matter, Cork or other light wood, unable, through its Levity, to superate the Crassitude of the water, and of that Matter should forme Solids of divers Figures, would in vain seek to find out what operation Figure hath in Natation or Submersion; because all would swim, and that not through any property of this or that Figure, but through the debility of the Matter, wanting so much Gravity, as is requisite to superate and overcome the Density and Crassitude of the water.

An Experiment in Ebany, brought to disprove the Experiment in Wax.

Its needfull, therefore, if wee would see the effect wrought by the Diversity of Figure, first to make choice of a Matter of its nature apt to penetrate the Crassitude of the water. And, for this effect, they have made choice of such a Matter, as fit, that being readily reduced into Sphericall Figure, goes to the Bottom; and it is Ebony, of which they afterwards making a small Board or Splinter, as thin as a Lath, have illustrated how that this, put upon the Surface of the water, rests there without descending to the Bottom: and making, on the otherside, of the same wood a Ball, no less than a hazell Nut, they shew, that this swims not, but descendes. From which Experiment, they think they may frankly conclude, that the Breadth of the Figure in the flat Lath or Board, is the cause of its not descending to the Bottom, forasmuch as a Ball of the same Matter, not different from the Board in any thing but in Figure, submergeth in the same water to the Bottom. The discourse and the Experiment hath really so much of probability and likely hood of truth in it, that it would be no wonder, if many perswaded by a certain cursory observation, should yield credit to it; neverthelesse, I think I am able to discover, how that it is not free from falacy.

Beginning, therefore, to examine one by one, all the particulars that

have

have been produced, I say, that Figures, as simple Figures, not only operate not in naturall things, but neither are they ever seperated from the Corporeall substance: nor have I ever alledged them stript of sensible Matter, like as also I freely admit, that in our endeavouring to examine the Diversity of Accidents, dependant upon the variety of Figures, it is necessary to apply them to Matters, which obstruct not the various operations of those various Figures: and I admit and grant, that I should do very ill, if I would experiment the influence of Acutenesse of edge with a Knife of Wax, applying it to cut an Oak, because there is no Acuteness in Wax able to cut that very hard wood. But yet such an Experiment of this Knife, would not be besides the purpose, to cut curded Milk, or other very yielding Matter: yea, in such like Matters, the Wax is more commodious than Steel; for finding the diversity depending upon Angles, more or less Acute, for that Milk is indifferently cut with a Raisor, and with a Knife, that hath a blunt edge. It needs, therefore, that regard be had, not only to the hardness, solidity or Gravity of Bodies, which under divers figures, are to divide and penetrate some Matters, but it forceth also, that regard be had, on the other side, to the Resistance of the Matters, to be divided and penetrated. But since I have in making the Experiment concerning our Contest, chosen a Matter which penetrates the Resistance of the water; and in all figures descendes to the Bottome, the Adversaries can charge me with no defect; yea, I have propounded so much a more excellent Method than they, in as much as I have removed all other Causes, of descending or not descending to the Bottom, and retained the only sole and pure variety of Figures, demonstrating that the same Figures all descende with the only alteration of a Grain in weight: which Grain being removed, they return to float and swim; it is not true, therefore, (resuming the Example by them introduced) that I have gon about to experiment the efficacy of Acuteness, in cutting with Matters unable to cut, but with Matters proportioned to our occasion; since they are subjected to no other variety, then that alone which depends on the Figure more or less acute.

Figure is unseperable from Corporeall Substance.

But let us proceed a little farther, and observe, how that indeed the Consideration, which, they say, ought to be had about the Election of the Matter, to the end, that it may be proportionate for the making of our experiment, is needlesly introduced, declaring by the example of Cutting, that like as Acuteness is insufficient to cut, unless when it is in a Matter hard and apt to superate the Resistance of the wood or other Matter, which we intend to cut; so the aptitude of descending or notdescending in water, ought and can only be known in those Matters, that are able to overcome the Renitence, and superate the Crassitude of the water. Unto which, I say, that to make distinction and election, more of this than of that Matter, on which to

The answer to the Objection against the Experiment of the Wax.

impress

impreſs the Figures for cutting or penetrating this or that Body, as the ſolidity or obdurateneſs of the ſaid Bodies ſhall be greater or leſs, is very neceſſary : but withall I ſubjoyn, that ſuch diſtinction, election and caution would be ſuperfluous and unprofitable, if the Body to be cut or penetrated, ſhould have no Reſiſtance, or ſhould not at all withſtand the Cutting or Penitration : and if the Knife were to be uſed in cutting a Miſt or Smoak, one of Paper would be equally ſerviceable with one of *Damaſcus* Steel : and ſo by reaſon the water hath not any Reſiſtance againſt the Penitration of any Solid Body, all choice of Matter is ſuperfluous and needleſs, and the Election which I ſaid above to have been well made of a Matter reciprocall in Gravity to water, was not becauſe it was neceſſary, for the overcoming of the craſſitude of the water, but its Gravity, with which only it reſiſts the ſinking of Solid Bodies : and for what concerneth the Reſiſtance of the craſſitude, if we narrowly conſider it, we ſhall find that all Solid Bodies, as well thoſe that ſink, as thoſe that ſwim, are indifferently accomodated and apt to bring us to the knowledge of the truth in queſtion. Nor will I be frighted out of the belief of theſe Concluſions, by the Experiments which may be produced againſt me, of many ſeverall Woods, Corks, Galls, and, moreover, of ſubtle ſlates and plates of all ſorts of Stone and Mettall, apt by means of their Naturall Gravity, to move towards the Centre of the Earth, the which, nevertheleſs, being impotent, either through the Figure (as the Adverſaries thinke) or through Levity, to break and penetrate the Continuity of the parts of the water, and to diſtract its union, do continue to ſwimm without ſubmerging in the leaſt : nor on the other ſide, ſhall the Authority of *Ariſtotle* move me, who in more than one place, affirmeth the contrary to this, which Experience ſhews me.

No Solid of ſuch Levity, nor of ſuch Figure, but that it doth penetrate the Craſſitude of the Water.

Bodies of all Figures, laid upon the water, do penetrate its Craſſitude, and in what proportion.

I return, therefore, to aſſert, that there is not any Solid of ſuch Levity, nor of ſuch Figure, that being put upon the water, doth not divide and penetrate its Craſſitude : yea if any with a more perſpicatious eye, ſhall return to obſerve more exactly the thin Boards of Wood, he ſhall ſee them to be with part of their thickneſs under water, and not only with their inferiour Superficies, to kiſſe the Superiour of the water, as they of neceſſity muſt have believed, who have ſaid, that ſuch Boards ſubmerge not, as not being able to divide the Tenacity of the parts of the water : and, moreover, he ſhall ſee, that ſubtle ſhivers of Ebony, Stone or Metall, when they float, have not only broak the Continuity of the water, but are with all their thickneſs, under the Surface of it; and more and more, according as the Matters are more grave : ſo that a thin Plate of Lead, ſhall be lower than the Surface of the circumfuſed water, by at leaſt twelve times the thickneſs of the Plate, and Gold ſhall dive

below

below the Levell of the water, almost twenty times the thicknefs of the Plate, as I fhall anon declare.

But let us proceed to evince, that the water yields and fuffers it felf to be penetrated by every the lighteft Body; and therewithall demonftrate, how, even by Matters that fubmerge not, we may come to know that Figure operates nothing about the going or not going to the Bottom, feeing that the water fuffers it felf to be penetrated equally by every Figure.

The Experiment of a Cone, demitted with its Bafe, and after with its Point downwards.

Make a Cone, or a Piramis of Cyprefs, of Firre, or of other Wood of like Gravity, or of pure Wax, and let its height be fomewhat great, namely a handfull, or more, and put it into the water with the Bafe downwards: firft, you fhall fee that it will penetrate the water, nor fhall it be at all impeded by the largenefs of the Bafe, nor yet fhall it fink all under water, but the part towards the point fhall lye above it: by which fhall be manifeft, firft, that that Solid forbeares not to fink out of an inabillity to divide the Continuity of the water, having already divided it with its broad part, that in the opinion of the Adverfaries is the lefs apt to make the divifion. The Piramid being thus fixed, note what part of it fhall be fubmerged, and revert it afterwards with the point downwards, and you fhall fee that it fhall not dive into the water more than before, but if you obferve how far it fhall fink, every perfon expert in Geometry, may meafure, that thofe parts that remain out of the water, both in the one and in the other Experiment are equall to an hair: whence he may manifeftly conclude, that the acute Figure which feemed moft apt to part and penetrate the water, doth not part or penetrate it more than the large and fpacious.

And he that would have a more eafie Experiment, let him take two Cylinders of the fame Matter, one long and fmall, and the other fhort, but very broad, and let him put them in the water, not diftended, but erect and endways: he fhall fee, if he diligently meafure the parts of the one and of the other, that in each of them the part fubmerged, retains exactly the fame proportion to that out of the water, and that no greater part is fubmerged of that long and fmall one, than of the other more fpacious and broad: howbeit, this refts upon a very large, and that upon a very little Superficies of water: therefore the diverfity of Figure, occafioneth neither facility, nor difficulty, in parting and penetrating the Continuity of the water; and, confequently, cannot be the Caufe of the Natation or Submerfion. He may likewife difcover the non operating of variety of Figures, in arifing from the Bottom of the water, towards the Surface, by taking Wax, and tempering it with a competent quantity of the filings of Lead, fo that it may become a confiderable matter graver than the water: then let him make

it

it into a Ball, and thrust it unto the Bottom of the water; and fasten to it as much Cork, or other light matter, as just serveth to raise it, and draw it towards the Surface : for afterwards changing the same Wax into a thin Cake, or into any other Figure, that same Cork shall raise it in the same manner to a hair.

This silenceth not my Antagonists, but they say, that all the discourse hitherto made by me little importeth to them, and that it serves their turn, that they have demonstrated in one only particular, and in what matter, and under what Figure pleaseth them, namely, in a Board and in a Ball of Ebony, that this put in the water, descends to the Bottom, and that stays atop to swim: and the Matter being the same, and the two Bodies differing in nothing but in Figure, they affirm, that they have with all perspicuity demonstrated and sensibly manifested what they undertook; and lastly, that they have obtained their intent. Nevertheless, I believe, and thinke, I can demonstrate, that that same Experiment proveth nothing against my Conclusion.

In Experiments of Natation, the Solid is to be put into, not upon the water.

And first, it is false, that the Ball descends, and the Board not: for the Board shall also descend, if you do to both the Figures, as the words of our Question requireth; that is, if you put them both into the water.

The Question of Natation stated.

The words were these. That the Antagonists having an opinion, that the Figure would alter the Solid Bodies, in relation to the descending or not descending, ascending or not ascending in the same Medium, *as* v. gr. *in the same water, in such sort, that, for Example, a Solid that being of a Sphericall Figure, shall descend to the Bottom, being reduced into some other Figure, shall not descend : I holding the contrary, do affirm, that a Corporeall Solid Body, which reduced into a Sphericall Figure, or any other, shall go to the Bottom, shall do the like under whatsoever other Figure, &c.*

Place defined according to Aristotle.

But to be in the water, implies to be placed in the water, and by *Aristotles* own Definition of place, to be placed, importeth to be invironed by the Superficies of the Ambient Body, therefore, then shall the two Figures be in the water, when the Superficies of the water, shall imbrace and inviron them : but when the Adversaries shew the Board of Ebony not descending to the Bottom, they put it not into the water, but upon the water, where being by a certain impediment (as by and by we will shew) retained, it is invironed, part by water, and part by air, which thing is contrary to our agreement, that was, that the Bodies should be in the water, and not part in water, and part in air.

The

The which is again made manifest, by the questions being put as well about the things which go to the Bottom, as those which arise from the Bottom to swimme, and who sees not that things placed in the Bottom, must have water about them.

It is now to be noted, that the Board of Ebany and the Ball, put into the water, both sink, but the Ball more swiftly, and the Board more slowly; and slower and slower, according as it shall be more broad and thin, and of this Tardity the breadth of the Figure is the true Cause: But these broad Boards that slowly descend, are the same, that being put lightly upon the water, do swimm: Therefore, if that were true which the Adversaries affirm, the same numerical Figure, would in the same numericall water, cause one while Rest, and another while Tardity of Motion, which is impossible: for every perticular Figure which descends to the Bottom, hath of necessity its own determinate Tardity and slowness, proper and naturall unto it, according to which it moveth, so that every other Tardity, greater or lesser is improper to its nature: if, therefore, a Board, as suppose of a foot square, descendeth naturally with six degrees of Tardity, it is impossible, that it should descend with ten or twenty, unless some new impediment do arrest it. Much less can it, by reason of the same Figure rest, and wholly cease to move; but it is necessary, that when ever it resteth, there do some greater impediment intervene than the breadth of the Figure. Therefore, it must be somewhat else, and not the Figure, that stayeth the Board of Ebany above water, of which Eigure the only Effect is the retardment of the Motion, according to which it descendeth more slowly than the Ball. Let it be confessed, therefore, rationally discoursing, that the true and sole Cause of the Ebanys going to the Bottom, is the excess of its Gravity above the Gravity of the water: and the Cause of the greater or less Tardity, the breadth of this Figure, or the contractedness of that: but of its Rest, it can by no means be allowed, that the quallity of the Figure, is the Cause thereof: aswell, because, making the Tardity greater, according as the Figure more dilateth, there cannot be so immense a Dilatation, to which there may not be found a correspondent immence Tardity without redusing it to Nullity of Motion; as, because the Figures produced by the Antagonists for effecters of Rest, are the self same that do also go to the Bottom.

The confutation of the Experiment in the Ebany.

Every perticular Figure hath its own peculiar Tardity.

I will not omit another reason, founded also upon Experience, and if I deceive not my self, manifestly concluding, how that the Introduction of the breadth or amplitude of Figure, and the Resistance of the water against penetration, have nothing to do in the Effect of descending, or ascending, or resting in the water. *Take a piece of wood or other Matter, of which a Ball ascends from the Bottom of the water to

* The Figure & Resistance of the Medium against Division, have nothing to do with the Effect of Natation or Submersion, by an Experiment in Wallnut tree.

to the Surface, more slowly than a Ball of Ebony of the same bignesse, so that it is manifest, that the Ball of Ebony more readily divideth the water in descending, than the other in ascending; as for Example, let the Wood be Walnut-tree. Then take a Board of Walnut-tree, like and equall to that of Ebony of the Antagonists, which swims; and if it be true, that this floats above water, by reason of the Figure, unable through its breadth, to pierce the Crassitude of the same, the other of Wallnut-tree, without all question, being thrust unto the Bottom, will stay there, as less apt, through the same impediment of Figure, to divide the said Resistance of the water. But if we shall find, and by experience see, that not only the thin Board, but every other Figure of the same Wallnut-tree will return to float, as undoubtedly we shall, then I must desier my opposers to forbear to attribute the floating of the Ebony, unto the Figure of the Board, in regard that the Resistance of the water is the same, as well to the ascent, as to the descent, and the force of the Wallnut-trees ascension, is lesse than the Ebonys force in going to the Bottom.

An Experiment in Gold, to prove the non-operating of Figure in Natation and Submersion.

Nay, I will say more, that if we shall consider Gold in comparison of water, we shall find, that it exceeds it in Gravity almost twenty times, so that the Force and Impetus, wherewith a Ball of Gold goes to the Bottom, is very great. On the contrary, there want not matters, as Virgins Wax, and some Woods, which are not above a fiftieth part less grave than water, whereupon their Ascension therein is very slow, and a thousand times weaker than the *Impetus* of the Golds descent: yet notwithstanding, a plate of Gold swims without descending to the Bottom, and, on the contrary, we cannot make a Cake of Wax, or thin Board of Wood, which put in the Bottom of the Water, shall rest there without ascending. Now if the Figure can obstruct the Penetration, and impede the descent of Gold, that hath so great an *Impetus*, how can it choose but suffice to resist the same Penetration of the other matter in ascending, when as it hath scarce a thousandth part of the *Impetus* that the Gold hath in descending? Its therefore, necessary, that that which suspends the thin Plate of Gold, or Board of Ebony, upon the water, be some thing that is wanting to the other Cakes and Boards of Matters less grave than the water; since that being put to the Bottom, and left at liberty, they rise up to the Surface, without any obstruction: But they want not for flatness and breadth of Figure: Therefore, the *spaciousnesse of the Figure, is not that which makes the Gold and Ebony to swim.

And, because, that the excess of their Gravity above the Gravity of the water, is questionless the Cause of the sinking of the flat piece of Ebony, and the thin Plate of Gold, when they go to the Bottom, therefore, of necessity, when they float, the Cause of their staying above water, proceeds from Levity, which in that case, by some Accident,

peradventure

peradventure not hitherto obſerved, cometh to meet with the ſaid Board, rendering it no longer as it was before, whilſt it did ſink more Ponderous than the water, but leſs.

Now, let us return to take the thin Plate of Gold, or of Silver, or the thin Board of Ebony, and let us lay it lightly upon the water, ſo that it ſtay there without ſinking, and diligently obſerve its effect. And firſt, ſee how falſe the aſſertion of *Ariſtotle*, and our oponents is, to wit, that it ſtayeth above water, through its unability to pierce and penetrate the Reſiſtance of the waters Craſſitude: for it will manifeſtly appear, not only that the ſaid Plates have penetrated the water, but alſo that they are a conſiderable matter lower than the Surface of the ſame, the which continueth eminent, and maketh as it were a Rampert on all ſides, round about the ſaid Plates, the profundity of which they ſtay ſwimming: and, according as the ſaid Plates ſhall be more grave than the water, two, four, ten or twenty times, it is neceſſary, that their Superficies do ſtay below the univerſall Surface of the water, ſo much more, than the thickneſs of thoſe Plates, as we ſhal more diſtinctly ſhew anon. In the mean ſpace, for the more eaſie underſtanding of what I ſay, obſerve with me a little the preſent Scheme: in which let us ſuppoſe the Surface of the water to be diſtended, according to the Lines F L D B, upon which if one ſhall put a board of matter ſpecifically more grave than water, but ſo lightly that it ſubmerge not, it ſhall not reſt any thing above, but ſhall enter with its whole thickneſs into the water: and, moreover, ſhall ſink alſo, as we ſee by the Board A I, O I, whoſe breadth is wholly ſunk into the water, the little Ramperts of water L A and D O incompaſſing it, whoſe Superficies is notably higher than the Superficies of the Board. See now whether it be true, that the ſaid Board goes not to the Bottom, as being of Figure unapt to penetrate the Craſſitude of the water.

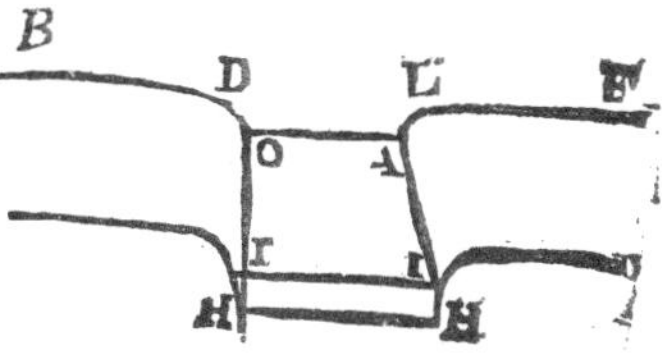

Why ſolids having penitrated the Water, do not proceed to a totall Submerſion.

But, if it hath already penetrated, and overcome the Continuity of the water, & is of its own nature more grave than the ſaid water, why doth it not proceed in its ſinking, but ſtop and ſuſpend its ſelf within that little dimple or cavitie, which with its ponderoſity it hath made in the water? I anſwer; becauſe that in ſubmerging it ſelf, ſo far as till its Superficies come to the Levell with that of the water, it loſeth a part of its Gravity, and loſeth the reſt of it as it ſubmergeth & deſcends beneath the Surface of the water, which maketh Ramperts and Banks round about it, and it ſuſtaines this loſs by means of its drawing after it, and carrying along with it, the Air that is above it, and by Contact adherent to it, which Air ſucceeds to fill the Cavity that is invironed by the Ramperts of water: ſo that that which in this caſe deſcends and is placed in the water, is not only the Board of Ebony or Plate of Iron, but a composition of Ebony and Air, from which resulteth a Solid no longer superiour in Gravity to the water, as was the simple Ebony, or the simple Gold. And, if we exactly consider, what, and how great the Solid is, that in this Experiment enters into the water, and contrasts with the Gravity of the same, it will be found to be all that which we find to be beneath the Surface of the water, the which is an aggregate and Compound of a Board of Ebony, and of almost the like quantity of Air, or a Mass compounded of a Plate of Lead, and ten or twelve times as much Air. But, Genrlemen, you that are my Antagonists in our Question, we require the Identity of Matter, and the alteration only of the Figure; therefore, you must remove that Air, which being conjoyned with the Board, makes it become another Body less grave than the Water, and put only the Ebony into the Water, and you shall certainly see the Board descend to the Bottom; and, if that do not happen, you have got the day. And to seperate the Air from the Ebony, there needs no more but only to bath the Superficies of the said Board with the same Water: for the Water being thus interposed between the Board and the Air, the other circumfused Water shall run together without any impediment, and shall receive into it the sole and bare Ebony, as it was to do.

How to seperate the Air from Solids in demitting them into the water.

But, me thinks I hear some of the Adversaries cunningly opposing this, and telling me, that they will not yield, by any means, that their Board be wetted, because the weight added thereto by the Water, by making it heavier than it was before, draws it to the Bottom, and that the addition of new weight is contrary to our agreement, which was, that the Matter be the same.

To this, I answer, first; that treating of the operation of Figure in Bodies put into the Water, none can suppose them to be put into the Water without being wet; nor do I desire more to be done to the Board, then I will give you leave to do to the Ball. Moreover, it is untrue, that the Board sinks by vertue of the new Weight added to it by the Water, in the single and slight bathing of it: for I will put ten or twenty drops of Water upon the same Board, whilst it is sustained upon the water; which drops, because not conjoyned with the other Water circumfused, shall not so encrease the weight of it, as to make it sink: but if the Board being taken out, and all the water wiped off that was added thereto, I should bath all its Superficies with one only very small drop, and put it again upon the water, without doubt it shall sink, the other Water running to cover it, not being retained by the superiour Air; which Air by the interposition of the thin vail of water, that takes away its Contiguity unto the Ebony, shall without Renitence be seperated, nor doth it in the least oppose the succession of the other Water: but rather, to speak better, it shall descend freely; because it shall be all environed and covered

with

with water, as soon as its superiour Superficies, before vailed with water, doth arrive to the Levell of the universall Surface of the said water. To say, in the next place, that water can encreale the weight of things that are demitted into it, is most false; for water hath no Gravity in water, since it descends not: yea, if we would well consider what any immense Mass of water doth put upon a grave Body; that is placed in it, we shall find experimentally, that it, on the contrary, will rather in a great part deminish the weight of it, and that we may be able to lift an huge Stone from the Bottom of the water, which the water being removed, we are not able to stir. Nor let them tell me by way of reply, that although the superposed water augment not the Gravity of things that are in it, yet it increaseth the ponderosity of those that swim, and are part in the water and part in the Air, as is seen, for Example, in a Brass Ketle, which whilst it is empty of water, and replenished only with Air shall swim, but pouring of Water therein, it shall become so grave, that it shall sink to the Bottom, and that by reason of the new weight added thereto. To this I will return answer, as above, that the Gravity of the Water, contained in the Vessel is not that which sinks it to the Bottom, but the proper Gravity of the Brass, superiour to the Specificall Gravity of the Water: for if the Vessel were less grave than water, the Ocean would not suffice to submerge it. And, give me leave to repeat it again, as the fundamentall and principall point in this Case, that the Air contained in this Vessel before the infusion of the Water, was that which kept it a-float, since that there was made of it, and of the Brass, a Composition less grave than an equall quantity of Water: and the place that the Vessel occupyeth in the Water whilst it floats, is not equall to the Brass alone, but to the Brass and to the Air together, which filleth that part of the Vessel that is below the Levell of the water: Moreover, when the Water is infused, the Air is removed, and there is a composition made of Brass and of water, more grave *in specie* than the simple water, but not by vertue of the water infused, as having greater Specifick Gravity than the other water, but through the proper Gravity of the Brass, and through the alienation of the Air. Now, as he that should say that Brass, that by its nature goes to the Bottom, being formed into the Figure of a Ketle, acquireth from that Figure a vertue of lying in the Water without sinking, would say that which is false; because that Brass fashioned into any whatever Figure, goeth always to the Bottom, provided, that that which is put into the water be simple Brass; and it is not the Figure of the Vessel that makes the Brass to float, but it is because that that is not purely Brass which is put into the water, but an aggregate of Brass and of Air: so is it neither more nor less false, that a thin Plate of Brass

Water hath no Gravity in Water.

Water deminisheth the Gravity of Solids immerged therein.

The Experiment of a brass Ketle swiming when empty, & sinking when full, alledged to prove that water gravitates in water, answered.

An Ocean sufficeth not to sink a Vessel specifically less grave than water.

Air, the Cause of the Natation of empty Vessels of Matters graver *in specie* than the water.

Neither Figure, nor the breadth of Figure, is the Cause of Natation.

or of Ebony, ſwims by vertue of its dilated & broad Figure: for the truth is, that it bares up without ſubmerging, becauſe that that which is put in the water, is not pure Braſs or ſimple Ebony, but an aggregate of Braſs and Air, or of Ebony and Air. And, this is not contrary unto my Concluſion, the which, (having many a time ſeen Veſſels of Mettall, and thin pieces of diverſe grave Matters float, by vertue of the Air conjoyned with them) did affirm, That Figure was not the Cauſe of the Natation or Submerſion of ſuch Solids as were placed in the water. Nay more, I cannot omit, but muſt tell my Antagoniſts, that this new conceit of denying that the Superficies of the Board ſhould be bathed, may beget in a third perſon an opinion of a poverty of Arguments of defence on their part, ſince that ſuch bathing was never inſiſted upon by them in the beginning of our Diſpute, and was not queſtioned in the leaſt, being that the Originall of the diſcourſe aroſe upon the ſwiming of Flakes of Ice, wherein it would be ſimplicity to require that their Superficies might be dry: beſides, that whether theſe pieces of Ice be wet or dry they alwayes ſwim, and as the Adverſaries ſay, by reaſon of the Figure.

Some peradventure, by way of defence, may ſay, that wetting the Board of Ebony, and that in the ſuperiour Superficies, it would, though of it ſelf unable to pierce and penetrate the water, be born downwards, if not by the weight of the additionall water, at leaſt by that deſire and propenſion that the ſuperiour parts of the water have to re-unite and rejoyn themſelves: by the Motion of which parts, the ſaid Board cometh in a certain manner, to be depreſſed downwards.

The Bathed Solid deſcends not out of any affectation of union in the upper parts of the water.

This weak Refuge will be removed, if we do but conſider, that the repugnancy of the inferiour parts of the water, is as great againſt Diſ-union, as the Inclination of its ſuperiour parts is to union: nor can the uper unite themſelves without depreſſing the board, nor can it deſcend without diſuniting the parts of the nether Water: ſo that it doth follow, by neceſſary conſequence, that for thoſe reſpects, it ſhall not deſcend. Moreover, the ſame that may be ſaid of the upper parts of the water, may with equall reaſon be ſaid of the nether, namely, that deſiring to unite, they ſhall force the ſaid Board upwards.

Happily, ſome of theſe Gentlemen that diſſent from me, will wonder, that I affirm, that the contiguous ſuperiour Air is able to ſuſtain that Plate of *Braſs* or of Silver, that ſtayeth above water; as if I would in a certain ſence allow the Air, a kind of Magnetick vertue of ſuſtaining the grave *Bodies*, with which it is contiguous. To ſatisfie all I may, to all doubts, I have been conſidering how by ſome other ſenſible Experiment I might demonſtrate, how truly that little contiguous and ſuperiour Air ſuſtaines thoſe Solids, which being by

A Magnetiſme in the *Air*, by which it bears up thoſe Solids in the water, that are contiguous with it.

nature

nature apt to descend to the Bottom, being placed lightly on the water submerge not, unless they be first thorowly bathed; and have found, that one of these Bodies having descended to the Bottom, by conveighing to it (without touching it in the least) a little Air, which conjoyneth with the top of the same; it becometh sufficient, not only, as before to sustain it, but also to raise it, and to carry it back to the top, where it stays and abideth in the same manner, till such time, as the assistance of the conjoyned Air is taken away. And to this effect, I have taken a Ball of Wax, and made it with a little Lead, so grave, that it leasurely descends to the Bottom, making with all its Superficies very smooth and pollite: and this being put gently into the water, almost wholly submergeth, there remaining visible only a little of the very top, the which so long as it is conjoyned with the Air, shall retain the Ball a-top, but the Contiguity of the Air taken away by wetting it, it shall descend to the Bottom and there remain. Now to make it by vertue of the Air, that before sustained it to return again to the top, and stay there, thrust into the water a Glass reversed with the mouth downwards, the which shall carry with it the Air it contains, and move this towards the Ball, abasing it till such time that you see, by the transparency of the Glass, that the contained Air do arrive to the summity of the *Ball*: then gently withdraw the Glass upwards, and you shall see the *Ball* to rise, and afterwards stay on the top of the water, if you carefully part the Glass and the water without overmuch commoving and disturbing it. There is, therefore, a certain affinity between the Air and other *Bodies*, which holds them united, so, that they seperate not without a kind of violence. The same likewise is seen in the water; for if we shall wholly submerge some *Body* in it, so that it be thorowly bathed, in the drawing of it afterwards gently out again, we shall see the water follow it, and rise notably above its Surface, before it seperates from it. Solid *Bodies*, also, if they be equall and alike in Superficies, so, that they make an exact Contact without the interposition of the least Air, that may part them in the seperation and yield untill that the ambient *Medium* succeeds to replenish the place, do hold very firmly conjoyned, and are not to be seperated without great force but, because, the Air, Water, and other Liquids, very expeditiously shape themselves to contact with any Solid *Bodies*, so that their Superficies do exquisitely adopt themselves to that of the Solids, without any thing remaining between them, therefore, the effect of this Conjunction and Adherence is more manifestly and frequently observed in them, than in hard and inflexible *Bodies*, whose Superficies do very rarely conjoyn with exactness of Contact. This is therefore that Magnetick vertue, which with firm Connection conjoyneth all Bodies, that do touch without the interposition of flexible fluids; and, who knows, but that that a Contact, when it is very exact, may be a sufficient Cause of the Union and Continuity of the parts of a naturall *Body*?

The Effect of the Airs Contiguity in the Natation of Solids.

The force of Contact.

An affectation of Conjunction betwixt Solids and the Air contiguous to them.

The like affectation of Conjunction betwixt Solids & the water.

Also the like affectation and Conjunction betwixt Solids themselves.

Contact may be the Cause of the Continuity of Naturall Bodies.

Now,

Now, pursuing my purpose, I say; that it needs not, that we have recourse to the Tenacity, that the parts of the water have amongst themselves, by which they resist and oppose Division, Distraction, and Seperation, because there is no such Coherence and Resistance of Division for if there were, it would be no less in the internall parts than in those nearer the superiour or externall Surface, so that the same Board, finding alwayes the same Resistance and Renitence, would no less stop in the middle of the water than about the Surface, which is false. Moreover, what Resistance can we place in the Continuity of the water, if we see that it is impossible to find any Body of whatsoever Matter, Figure or Magnitude, which being put into the water, shall be obstructed and impeded by the Tenacity of the parts of the water to one another, so, but that it is moved upwards or downwards, according as the Cause of their Motion transports it? And, what greater proof of it can we desier, than that which we daily see in Muddy waters, which being put into Vessels to be drunk, and being, after some hours setling, still, as we say, thick in the end, after four or six dayes they are wholly setled, and become pure and clear? Nor can their Resistance of Penetration stay those impalpable and insensible Atomes of Sand, which by reason of their exceeding small force, spend six dayes in descending the space of half a yard.

The settlement of *Muddy* Water, proveth that that Element hath no aversion to Division.

Nor let them say, that the seeing of such small Bodies, consume six dayes in descending so little a way, is a sufficient Argument of the Waters Resistance of Division; because that is no resisting of Division, but a retarding of Motion; and it would be simplicity to say, that a thing opposeth Division, and that in the same instant, it permits it self to be divided : nor doth the Retardation of Motion at all favour the Adversaries cause, for that they are to instance in a thing that wholly prohibiteth Motion, and procureth Rest; it is necessary, therefore, to find out Bodies that stay in the water, if one would shew its repugnancy to Division, and not such as move in it, howbeit but slowly.

Water cannot oppose division, and at the same time permit it self to be divided.

What then is this Crassitude of the water, with which it resisteth Division? What, I beseech you, should it be, if we (as we have said above) with all diligence attempting the reduction of a Matter into so like a Gravity with the water, that forming it into a dilated Plate it rests suspended as we have said, between the two waters, it be impossible to effect it, though we bring them to such an Equiponderance, that as much Lead as the fourth part of a Grain of Musterd-seed, added to the same expanded Plate, that in Air [*i. e. out of the water*] shall weigh four or six pounds, sinketh it to the Bottom, and being substracted, it ascends to the Surface of the water? I cannot see, (if what I say be true, as it is most certain) what minute vertue and force we can possibly find or imagine, to which the Resistance of the water against Division and Penetration

tion is not inferiour; whereupon, we must of necessity conclude that it is nothing: because, if it were of any sensible power, some large Plate might be found or compounded of a Matter alike in Gravity to the water, which not only would stay between the two waters; but, moreover, should not be able to descend or ascend without notable force. We may likewise collect the same from an other Experiment, shewing that the Water gives way also in the same manner to transversall Division; for if in a setled and standing water we should place any great Mass that goeth not to the bottom, drawing it with a single Womans Hair, we might carry it from place to place without any opposition, and this whatever Figure it hath, though that it possess a great space of water, as for instance, a great Beam would do moved side-ways. Perhaps some might oppose me and say, that if the Resistance of water against Division, as I affirm, were nothing; Ships should not need such a force of Oars and Sayles for the moving of them from place to place in a tranquile Sea, or standing Lake. To him that should make such an objection, I would reply, that the water contrasteth not against, nor simply resisteth Division, but a sudden Division, and with so much greater Renitence, by how much greater the Velocity is: and the Cause of this Resistance depends not on Crassitude, or any other thing that absolutely opposeth Division, but because that the parts of the water divided, in giving way to that Solid that is moved in it, are themselves also necessitated locally to move, some to the one side, and some to the other, and some downwards: and this must no less be done by the waves before the Ship, or other Body swimming through the water, than by the posteriour and subsequent; because, the Ship proceeding forwards, to make it self a way to receive its Bulk, it is requisite, that with the Prow it repulse the adjacent parts of the water, as well on one hand as on the other, and that it move them as much transversly, as is the half of the breadth of the Hull: and the like removall must those waves make, that succeeding the Poump do run from the remoter parts of the Ship towards those of the middle, successively to replenish the places, which the Ship in advancing forwards, goeth, leaving vacant. Now, because, all Motitions are made in Time, and the longer in greater time: and it being moreover true, that those Bodies that in a certain time are moved by a certain power such a certain space, shall not be moved the same space, and in a shorter Time, unless by a greater Power: therefore, the broader Ships move slower than the narrower, being put on by an equall Force: and the same Vessel requires so much greater force of Wind, or Oars, the faster it is to move.

An Hair will draw a great Mass thorow the Water; which proveth, that it hath no Resistance against transversall Division.

How ships are moved in the water.

Bodies moved a certain space in a certain Time, by a certain power, cannot be moved the same space, and in a shorter time, but by a greater power.

But yet for all this, any great Mass swimming in a standing Lake, may be moved by any petit force; only it is true, that a lesser force more slowly moves it: but if the waters Resistance of Division, were in any manner sensible, it would follow, that the said Mass, should, notwithstanding the percussion of some sensible force, continue immoveable, which is not so. Yea, I will say farther, that should we retire our selves into the more internall contemplation of the Nature of water and other Fluids, perhaps we should discover the Constitution of their parts to be such, that they not only do not oppose Division, but that they have not any thing in them to be divided: so that the Resistance that is observed in moving through the water, is like to that which we meet with in passing through a great Throng of People, wherein we find impediment, and not by any difficulty in the Division, for that none of those persons are divided whereof the Croud is composed, but only in moving of those persons sideways which were before divided and disjoyned: and thus we find Resistance in thrusting a Stick into an heap of Sand, not because any part of the Sand is to be cut in pieces, but only to be moved and raised. Two manners of Penetration, therefore, offer themselves to us, one in Bodies, whose parts were continuall, and here Division seemeth necessary; the other in the aggregates of parts not continuall, but contiguous only, and here there is no necessity of dividing but of moving only. Now, I am not well resolved, whether water and other Fluids may be esteemed to be of parts continuall or contiguous only; yet I find my self indeed inclined to think that they are rather contiguous (if there be in Nature no other manner of aggregating, than by the union, or by the touching of the extreams:) and I am induced thereto by the great difference that I see between the Conjunction of the parts of an hard or Solid Body, and the Conjunction of the same parts when the same Body shall be made Liquid and Fluid: for if, for example, I take a Mass of Silver or other Solid and hard Mettall, I shall in dividing it into two parts, find not only the resistance that is found in the moving of it only, but an other incomparably greater, dependent on that vertue, whatever it be, which holds the parts united: and so if we would divide again those two parts into other two, and successively into others and others, we should still find a like Resistance, but ever less by how much smaller the parts to be divided shall be; but if, lastly, employing most subtile and acute Instruments, such as are the most tenuous parts of the Fire, we shall resolve it (perhaps) into its last and least Particles, there shall not be left in them any longer either Resistance of Division, or so much as a capacity of being farther divided, especially by Instruments more grosse than the acuities of Fire: and what Knife or Rasor put into well melted Silver can we finde, that will divide a thing which surpasseth the separating power of Fire? Certainly none: because either the whole shall be reduced to the most minute and ultimate Divisions, or if there remain parts capable still of other Subdivisions,

> The parts of Liquids, so farre from resisting Division, that they contain not any thing that may be divided.

> The Resistance a Solid findeth in moving through the water, like to that we meet with in passing through a throng of people:

> Or in thrusting a Stick into an heap of Sand.

> Two kinds of Penetration, one in Bodies continuall, the other in Bodies only contiguous.

> Water consists not of continuall, but only of contiguous parts.

> *See what satisfaction he hath given, as to this point, in Lib. de Motu. Dial. 2.*

> Great difference betwixt the Conjunction of the parts of a Body when Solid, and when fluid.

divisions, they cannot receive them, but only from acuter Divisors than Fire; but a Stick or Rod of Iron, moved in the melted Metall, is not such a one. Of a like Constitution and Consistence, I account the parts of Water, and other Liquids to be, namely, incapable of Division by reason of their Tenuity; or if not absolutely indivisible, yet at least not to be divided by a Board, or other Solid Body, palpable unto the hand, the Sector being alwayes required to be more sharp than the Solid to be cut. Solid Bodies, therefore, do only move, and not divide the Water, when put into it; whose parts being before divided to the extreamest minuity, and therefore capable of being moved, either many of them at once, or few, or very few, they soon give place to every small Corpuscle, that descends in the same: for that, it being little and light, descending in the Air, and arriving to the Surface of the Water, it meets with Particles of Water more small, and of less Resistance against Motion and Extrusion, than is its own prement and extrusive force, whereupon it submergeth, and moveth such a portion of them, as is proportionate to its Power. There is not, therefore, any Resistance in Water against Division, nay, there is not in it any divisible parts. I adde, moreover, that in case yet there should be any small Resistance found (which is absolutely false) haply in attempting with an Hair to move a very great natant Machine, or in essaying by the addition of one small Grain of Lead to sink, or by removall of it to raise a very broad Plate of Matter, equall in Gravity with Water, (which likewise will not happen, in case we proceed with dexterity) we may observe that that Resistance is a very different thing from that which the Adversaries produce for the Cause of the Natation of the Plate of Lead or Board of Ebony, for that one may make a Board of Ebony, which being put upon the Water swimmeth, and cannot be submerged, no not by the addition of an hundred Grains of Lead put upon the same, and afterwards being bathed, not only sinks, though the said Lead be taken away, but though moreover a quantity of Cork, or of some other light Body fastened to it, sufficeth not to hinder it from sinking unto the bottome: so that you see, that although it were granted that there is a certain small Resistance of Division found in the substance of the Water, yet this hath nothing to do with that Cause which supports the Board above the Water, with a Resistance an hundred times greater than that which men can find in the parts of the Water: nor let them tell me, that only the Surface of the Water hath such Resistance, and not the internall parts, or that such Resistance is found greatest in the beginning of the Submersion, as it also seems that in the beginning, Motion meets with greater opposition, than in the continuance of it; because, first, I will permit, that the Water be stirred, and that the superiour parts be mingled with the middle, and inferiour parts, or that those above be wholly removed, and those in the middle only made use off, and yet you shall see the effect for all

Water consists of parts that admit of no farther division.

Solids dimitted into the water, do onely move, and not divide it.

If there were any Resistance of Division in water, it must needs be small, in that it is overcome by an Hair, a Grain of Lead, or a slight bathing of the Solid.

The uper parts of the Water, do no more resist Division than the middle or lowest parts.

Waters Resistance of division, not greater in the beginning of the Submersion.

all that, to be still the same : Moreover, that Hair which draws a Beam through the Water, is likewise to divide the upperparts, and is also to begin the Motion, and yet it begins it, and yet it divides it : and finally, let the Board of Ebony be put in the midway, betwixt the bottome and the top of the Water, and let it there for a while be suspended and setled, and afterwards let it be left at liberty, and it will instantly begin its Motion, and will continue it unto the bottome. Nay, more, the Board so soon as it is dimitted upon the Water, hath not only begun to move and divide it, but is for a good space dimerged into it.

Let us receive it, therefore, for a true and undoubted Conclusion, That the Water hath not any Renitence against simple Division, and that it is not possible to find any Solid Body, be it of what Figure it will, which being put into the Water, its Motion upwards or downwards, according as it exceedeth, or shall be exceeded by the Water in Gravity (although such excesse and difference be insensible) shall be prohibited, and taken away, by the Crassitude of the said Water. When, therefore, we see the Board of Ebony, or of other Matter, more grave than the Water, to stay in the Confines of the Water and Air, without submerging, we must have recourse to some other Originall, for the investing the Cause of that Effect, than to the breadth of the Figure, unable to overcome the Renitence with which the Water opposeth Division, since there is no Resistance ; and from that which is not in being, we can expect no Action. It remains most true, therefore, as we have said before, that this so succeeds, for that that which in such manner put upon the water, not the same Body with that which is put *into* the Water: because this which is put *into* the Water, is the pure Board of Ebony, which for that it is more grave than the Water, sinketh, and that which is put *upon* the Water, is a Composition of Ebony, and of so much Air, that both together are specifically less grave than the Water, and therefore they do not descend.

I will farther confirm this which I say. Gentlemen, my Antagonists, we are agreed, that the excess or defect of the Gravity of the Solid, unto the Gravity of the Water, is the true and proper Cause of Natation or Submersion.

Great Caution to be had in experimenting the operation of Figure in Natation.

Now, if you will shew that besides the former Cause, there is another which is so powerfull, that it can hinder and remove the Submersion of those very Solids, that by their Gravity sink, and if you will say, that this is the breadth or ampleness of Figure, you are obliged, when ever you would shew such an Experiment, first to make the circumstances certain, that that Solid which you put into the Water, be not less grave *in specie* than it, for if you should not do so, any one might with reason say, that not the Figure, but the Levity was the cause of that Natation. But I say, that when you shall dimit

mit a Board of Ebony into the Water, you do not put therein a Solid more grave *in specie* than the Water, but one lighter, for besides the Ebony, there is in the Water a Mass of Air, united with the Ebony, and such, and so light, that of both there results a Composition less grave than the Water: See, therefore, that you remove the Air, and put the Ebony alone into the Water, for so you shall immerge a Solid more grave then the Water, and if this shall not go to the Bottom, you have well Philosophized, and I ill.

Now, since we have found the true Cause of the Natation of those Bodies, which otherwise, as being graver than the Water, would descend to the bottom, I think, that for the perfect and distinct knowledge of this business, it would be good to proceed in a way of discovering demonstratively those particular Accidents that do attend these effects, and,

PROBL. I.

To finde what proportion severall Figures of different Matters ought to have, unto the Gravity of the Water, that so they may be able by vertue of the Contiguous Air to stay afloat.

To finde the proportion Figures ought to have to the waters Gravity, that by help of the contiguous Air, they may swim.

LEt, therefore, for better illustration, D F N E be a Vessell, wherein the water is contained, and suppose a Plate or Board, whose thickness is comprehended between the Lines I C and O S, and let it be of Matter exceeding the water in Gravity, so that being put upon the water, it dimergeth and abaseth below the Levell of the said water, leaving the little Banks A I and B C, which are at the greatest height they can be, so that if the Plate I S should but descend any little space farther, the little Banks or Ramparts would no longer consist, but expulsing the Air A I C B, they would diffuse themselves over the Superficies I C, and would submerge the Plate. The height AIBC is therefore the greatest profundity that the little Banks of water admit of. Now I say, that from this, and from the proportion in Gravity, that the Matter of the Plate hath to the water, we may easily finde of what thickness, at most, we may make the said Plates, to the end, they may be able to bear up above water: for if the Matter of the Plate or Board I S were, for Example, as heavy again as the water, a Board of that Matter shall be, at the most of a thickness equall to the greatest height of the Banks, that is, as thick as A I is high: which we will thus demonstrate. Let the Solid I S be double in Gravity to the water, and let it be a regular

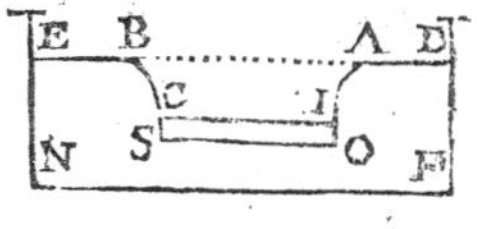

E B A D
C I
N S O F

Prisme

Prisme, or Cylinder, to wit, that hath its two flat Superficies, superiour and inferiour, alike and equall, and at Right Angles with the other laterall Superficies, and let its thicknes IO be equall to the greatest Altitude of the Banks of water: I say, that if it be put upon the water, it will not submerge: for the Altitude AI being equall to the Altitude IO, the Mass of the Air ABCI shall be equall to the Mass of the Solid CIOS: and the whole Mass AOSB double to the Mass IS; And since the Mass of the Air AC, neither encreaseth nor diminisheth the Gravity of the Mass IS, and the Solid IS was supposed double in Gravity to the water; Therefore as much water as the Mass submerged AOSB, compounded of the Air AICB, and of the Solid IOSC, weighs just as much as the same submerged Mass AOSB: but when such a Mass of water, as is the submerged part of the Solid, weighs as much as the said Solid, it descends not farther, but resteth, as by (a) *Archimedes*, and above by us, hath been demonstrated: Therefore, IS shall descend no farther, but shall rest. And if the Solid IS shall be Sesquialter in Gravity to the water, it shall float, as long as its thicknes be not above twice as much as the greatest Altitude of the Ramparts of water, that is, of AI. For IS being Sesquialter in Gravity to the water, and the Altitude OI, being double to IA, the Solid submerged AOSB, shall be also Sesquialter in Mass to the Solid IS. And because the Air AC, neither increaseth nor diminisheth the ponderosity of the Solid IS: Therefore, as much water in quantity as the submerged Mass AOSB, weighs as much as the said Mass submerged: And, therefore, that Mass shall rest. And briefly in generall.

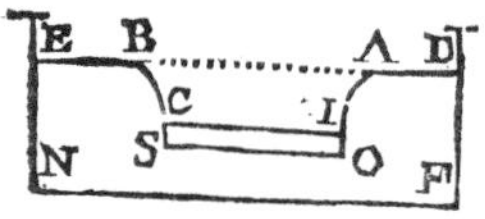

(a) Of Natation Lib. 1. Prop. 3.

THEOREME. VI.

The proportion of the greatest thicknes of Solids, beyond which encreased they sink.

When ever the excess of the Gravity of the Solid above the Gravity of the Water, shall have the same proportion to the Gravity of the Water, that the Altitude of the Rampart, hath to the thicknes of the Solid, that Solid shall not sink, but being never so little thicker it shall.

LEt the Solid IS be superior in Gravity to the water, and of such thicknes, that the Altitude of the Rampart AI, be in proportion to the thicknes of the Solid IO, as the excess of the Gravity of the said Solid IS, above the Gravity of a Mass of water equall to the Mass IS, is to the Gravity of the Mass of water equall to the Mass

Mass I S. I say, that the Solid I S shall not sinke, but being never so little thicker it shall go to the bottom : For being that as A I is to I O, so is the Excess of the Gravity of the Solid I S, above the Gravity of a Mass of water equall to the Mass I S, to the Gravity of the said Mass of water : Therefore, compounding, as A O is to O I, so shall the Gravity of the Solid I S, be to the Gravity of a Mass of water equall to the Mass I S: And, converting, as I O is to O A, so shall the Gravity of a Mass of water equall to the Mass I S, be to the Gravity of the Solid I S : But as I O is to O A, so is a Mass of water I S, to a Mass of water equall to the Mass A B S O : and so is the Gravity of a Mass of water I S, to the Gravity of a Mass of water A S: Therefore as the Gravity of a Mass of water, equall to the Mass I S, is to the Gravity of the Solid I S, so is the same Gravity of a Mass of water I S, to the Gravity of a Mass of Water A S: Therefore the Gravity of the Solid I S, is equall to the Gravity of a Mass of water equall to the Mass A S: But the Gravity of the Solid I S, is the same with the Gravity of the Solid A S, compounded of the Solid I S, and of the Air A B C I. Therefore the whole compounded Solid A O S B, weighs as much as the water that would be comprised in the place of the said Compound A O S B : And, therefore, it shall make an *Equilibrium* and rest, and that same Solid I O S C shall sinke no farther. But if its thickness I O should be increased, it would be necessary also to encrease the Altitude of the Rampart A I, to maintain the due proportion : But by what hath been supposed, the Altitude of the Rampart A I, is the greatest that the Nature of the Water and Air do admit, without the waters repulsing the Air adherent to the Superficies of the Solid I C, and possessing the space A I C B : Therefore, a Solid of greater thickness than I O, and of the same Matter with the Solid I S, shall not rest without submerging, but shall descend to the bottome : which was to be demonstrated.

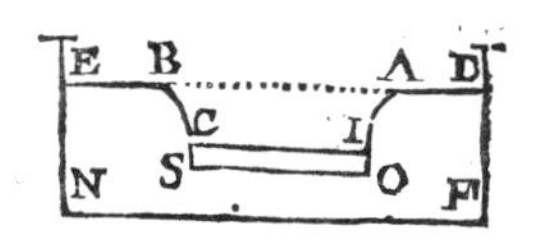

In consequence of this that hath been demonstrated, sundry and various Conclusions may be gathered, by which the truth of my principall Proposition comes to be more and more confirmed, and the imperfection of all former Argumentations touching the present Question cometh to be discovered.

And first we gather from the things demonstrated, that,

THEOREME. VII.

The heaviest Bodies may swimme.

All Matters, how heavy soever, even to Gold it self, the heaviest of all Bodies, known by us, may float upon the Water.

BEcause its Gravity being considered to be almost twenty times greater than that of the water, and, moreover, the greatest Altitude that the Rampart of water can be extended to, without breaking the Contiguity of the Air, adherent to the Surface of the Solid, that is put upon the water being predetermined, if we should make a Plate of Gold so thin, that it exceeds not the nineteenth part of the Altitude of the said Rampart, this put lightly upon the water shall rest, without going to the bottom: and if Ebony shall chance to be in sesquiseptimall proportion more grave than the water, the greatest thicknes that can be allowed to a Board of Ebony, so that it may be able to stay above water without sinking, would be seaven times more than the height of the Rampart Tinn, *v. gr.* eight times more grave than water, shall swimm as oft as the thicknes of its Plate, exceeds not the 7th part of the Altitude of the Rampart.

He elsewhere cites this as a Proposition, therefore I make it of that number.

And here I will not omit to note, as a second Corrollary dependent upon the things demonstrated, that,

THEOREME VIII.

Natation and Submersion, collected from the thicknes, excluding the length and breadth of Plates.

The Expansion of Figure not only is not the Cause of the Natation of those grave Bodies, which otherwise do submerge, but also the determining what be those Boards of Ebony, or Plates of Iron or Gold that will swimme, depends not on it, rather that same determination is to be collected from the only thicknes of those Figures of Ebony or Gold, wholly excluding the consideration of length and breadth, as having no wayes any share in this Effect.

IT hath already been manifested, that the only cause of the Natation of the said Plates, is the reduction of them to be less grave than the water, by means of the connexion of that Air, which descendeth together with them, and possesseth place in the water; which place so occupyed, if before the circumfused water diffuseth it self to fill it, it be capable of as much water, as shall weigh equall with the Plate, the Plate shall remain suspended, and sinke no farther.

Now

Now let us see on which of these three dimensions of the Solid depends the terminating, what and how much the Mass of that ought to be, that so the assistance of the Air contiguous unto it, may suffice to render it specifically less grave than the water, whereupon it may rest without Submersion. It shall undoubtedly be found, that the length and breadth have not any thing to do in the said determination, but only the height, or if you will the thickness: for, if we take a Plate or Board, as for Example, of Ebony, whose Altitude hath unto the greatest possible Altitude of the Rampart, the proportion above declared, for which cause it swims indeed, but yet not if we never so little increase its thickness; I say, that retaining its thickness, and encreasing its Superficies to twice, four times, or ten times its bigness, or dminishing it by dividing it into four, or six, or twenty, or a hundred parts, it shall still in the same manner continue to float: but encreasing its thickness only a Hairs breadth, it will alwaies submerge, although we should multiply the Superficies a hundred and a hundred times. Now forasmuch as that this is a Cause, which being added, we adde also the Effect, and being removed, it is removed; and by augmenting or lessening the length or breadth in any manner, the effect of going, or not going to the bottom, is not added or removed: I conclude, that the greatness and smalness of the Superficies hath no influence upon the Natation or Submersion. And that the proportion of the Altitude of the Ramparts of Water, to the Altitude of the Solid, being constituted in the manner aforesaid, the greatness or smalness of the Superficies, makes not any variation, is manifest from that which hath been above demonstrated, and from this, that, *The Prisms and Cylinders which have the same Base, are in proportion to one another as their heights.* Whence Cylinders or Prismes, namely, the Board, be they great or little, so that they be all of equall thickness, have the same proportion to their Conterminall Air, which hath for Base the said Superficies of the Board, and for height the Ramparts of water; so that alwayes of that Air, and of the Board, Solids are compounded, that in Gravity equall a Mass of water equall to the Mass of the Solids, compounded of Air, and of the Board: whereupon all the said Solids do in the same manner continue afloat. We will conclude in the third place, that,

Prismes and Cylinders having the same Base, are to one another as their heights.

THEOREME. IX.

All Figures of all Matters, float by hep of the Rampart replenished with Air, and some but only touch the water.

All sorts of Figures of whatsoever Matter, albeit more grave than the Water, do by Benefit of the said Rampart, not only float, but some Figures, though of the gravest Matter, do stay wholly above Water, wetting only the inferiour Surface that toucheth the Water.

AND these shall be all Figures, which from the inferiour Base upwards, grow lesser and lesser; the which we shall exemplifie for this time in Piramides or Cones, of which Figures the passions are common. We will demonstrate therefore, that,

It is possible to form a Piramide, of any whatsoever Matter preposed, which being put with its Base upon the Water, rests not only without submerging, but without wetting it more then its Base.

For the explication of which it is requisite, that we first demonstrate the subsequent Lemma, namely, that,

LEMMA II.

Solids whose Masses are in contrary proportion to their Specifick Gravities, are equall in absolute Gravity.

Solids whose Masses answer in proportion contrarily to their Specificall Gravities, are equall in Absolute Gravities.

LEt A C and B be two Solids, and let the Mass A C be to the Mass B, as the Specificall Gravity of the Solid B, is to the Specificall Gravity of the Solid A C: I say, the Solids A C and B are equall in absolute weight, that is, equally grave. For if the Mass A C be equall to the Mass B, then, by the Assumption, the Specificall Gravity of B, shall be equall to the Specificall Gravity of A C, and being equall in Mass, and of the same Specificall Gravity they shall absolutely weigh one as much as another.

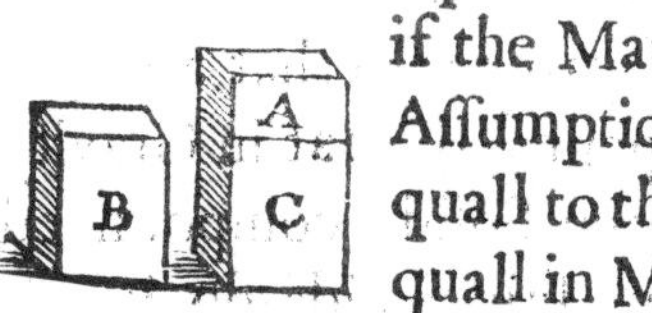

But if their Masses shall be unequall, let the Mass A C be greater, and in it take the part C, equall to the Mass B. And, because the Masses B and C are equall; the Absolute weight of B, shall have the same proportion to the Absolute weight of C, that the Specificall Gravity of B, hath to the Specificall Gravity of C; or of C A, which is the same *in specie*: But look what proportion the Specificall Gravity of B, hath to the Specificall Gravity of C A, the like proportion, by the Assumption, hath the Mass C A, to the Mass B; that is, to the Mass C: Therefore,

Therefore, the abſolute weight of B, to the abſolute weight of C, is as the Maſs A C to the Maſs *C* : But as the Maſs AC, is to the Maſs C, ſo is the abſolute weight of A C, to the abſolute weight of C : Therefore the abſolute weight of B, hath the ſame proportion to the abſolute weight of C, that the abſolute weight of A C, hath to the abſolute weight of C : Therefore, the two Solids A C and B are equall in abſolute Gravity : which was to be demonſtrated. Having demonſtrated this, I ſay,

THEOREME X.

That it is poſſible of any aſſigned Matter, to form a Piramide or Cone upon any Baſe, which being put upon the Water ſhall not ſubmerge, nor wet any more than its Baſe.

There may be Cones and Piramides of any *Matter*, which demitted into the water, reſt only their Baſes.

LEt the greateſt poſſible Altitude of the Rampart be the Line D B, and the Diameter of the Baſe of the Cone to be made of any Matter aſſigned B C, at right angles to D B : And as the Specificall Gravity of the Matter of the Piramide or Cone to be made, is to the Specificall Gravity of the water, ſo let the Altitude of the Rampart D B, be to the third part of the Piramide or Cone A B C, deſcribed upon the Baſe, whoſe Diameter is B C : I ſay, that the ſaid Cone A B C, and any other Cone, lower then the ſame, ſhall reſt upon the Surface of the water B C without ſinking. Draw D F parallel to B C, and ſuppoſe the Priſme or Cylinder E C, which ſhall be tripple to the Cone A B C.

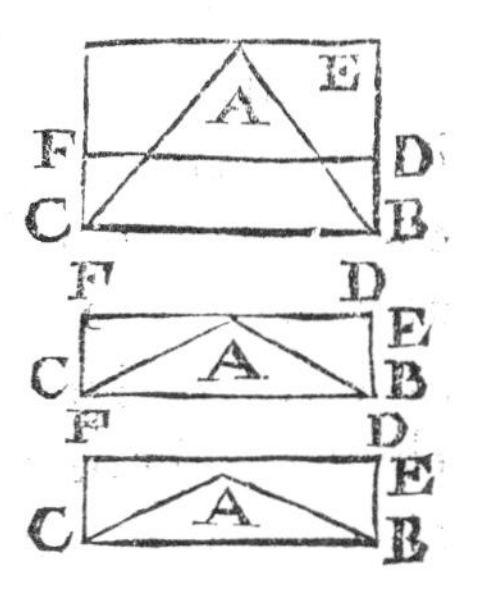

And, becauſe the Cylinder D C hath the ſame proportion to the Cylinder C E, that the Altitude D B, hath to the Altitude B E: But the Cylinder C E, is to the Cone A B C, as the Altitude E B is to the third part of the Altitude of the Cone : Therefore, by Equality of proportion, the Cylinder D C is to the Cone A B C, as D B is to the third part of the Altitude B E : But as D B is to the third part of B E, ſo is the Specificall Gravity of the Cone A B C, to the Specificall Gravity of the water : Therefore, as the Maſs of the Solid D C, is to the Maſs of the Cone A *B* C, ſo is the Specificall Gravity of the ſaid Cone, to the Specificall Gravity of the water : Therefore, by the precedent Lemma, the Cone A B C weighs in abſolute Gravity, as much as a Maſs of Water equall to the Maſs D C : But the water which by the impoſition of the Cone A B C, is driven out of its place, is as much as would preciſely lie in the place D C, and is equall in weight to the Cone that diſplaceth it : Therefore, there ſhall be an *Equilibrium*, and the Cone ſhall reſt without farther ſubmerging. And its manifeſt,

COROLARY I.

Amongst Cones of the same Base, those of least Altitude shall sink the least.

That making upon the same Basis, a Cone of a less Altitude, it shall be also less grave, and shall so much the more rest without Submersion.

COROLARY II.

There may be Cones and Piramides of any Matter, which demitted with the Point downwards do float a-top.

It is manifest, also, that one may make Cones and Piramids of any Matter whatsoever, more grave than the water, which being put into the water, with the Apix or Point downwards, rest without Submersion.

BEcause if we reassume what hath been above demonstrated, of Prisms and Cylinders, and that on Bases equall to those of the said Cylinders, we make Cones of the same Matter, and three times as high as the Cylinders, they shall rest afloat, for that in Mass and Gravity they shall be equall to those Cylinders, and by having their Bases equall to those of the Cylinders, they shall leave equall Masses of Air included within the Ramparts. This, which for Example sake hath been demonstrated, in Prisms, Cylinders, Cones and Piramids, might be proved in all other Solid Figures, but it would require a whole Volume (such is the multitude and variety of their Symptoms and Accidents) to comprehend the particuler demonstration of them all, and of their severall Segments: but I will to avoid prolixity in the present Discourse, content my self, that by what I have declared every one of ordinary Capacity may comprehend, that there is not any Matter so grave, no not Gold it self, of which one may not form all sorts of Figures, which by vertue of the superiour Air adherent to them, and not by the Waters Resistance of Penetration, do remain afloat, so that they sink not. Nay, farther, I will shew, for removing that Error, that,

THEOREME XI.

A Piramide or Cone, demitted with the Point downwards shal swim, with its Base downward shall sink.

A Piramide or Cone put into the Water, with the Point downward shall swimme, and the same put with the Base downwards shall sinke, and it shall be impossible to make it float.

NOw the quite contrary would happen, if the difficulty of Penetrating the water, were that which had hindred the descent, for that the said Cone is far apter to pierce and penetrate with its sharp Point, than with its broad and spacious Base.

And, to demonstrate this, let the Cone be *A B C*, twice as grave as the water, and let its height be tripple to the height of the Rampart *D A E C*: I say, first, that being put lightly into the water with the Point

Point downwards, it ſhall not deſcend to the bottom: for the Aeriall Cylinder contained betwixt the Ramparts *D A C E*, is equall in Maſs to the Cone *A B C*; ſo that the whole Maſs of the Solid compounded of the Air *D A C E*, and of the Cone *A B C*, ſhall be double to the Cone *A C B*: And, becauſe the Cone *A B C* is ſuppoſed to be of Matter double in Gravity to the water, therefore as much water as the whole Maſſe *D A B C E*, placed beneath the Levell of the water, weighs as much as the Cone *A B C*: and, therefore, there ſhall be an *Equilibrium*, and the Cone *A B C* ſhall deſcend no lower. Now, I ſay farther, that the ſame Cone placed with the Baſe downwards, ſhall ſink to the bottom, without any poſſibility of returning again, by any means to ſwimme.

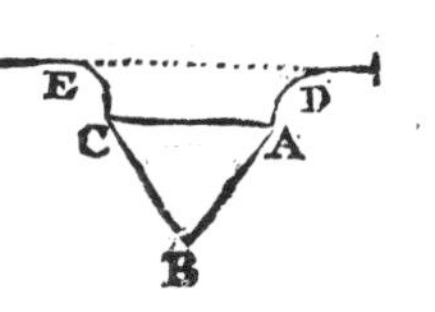

Let, therefore, the Cone be *A B D*, double in Gravity to the water, and let its height be tripple the height of the Rampart of water L B: It is already manifeſt, that it ſhall not ſtay wholly out of the water, becauſe the Cylinder being comprehended betwixt the Ramparts *L B D P*, equall to the Cone *A B D*, and the Matter of the Cone, beig double in Gravity to the water, it is evident that the weight of the ſaid Cone ſhall be double to the weight of the Maſs of water equall to the Cylinder *L B D P*: Therefore it ſhall not reſt in this ſtate, but ſhall deſcend.

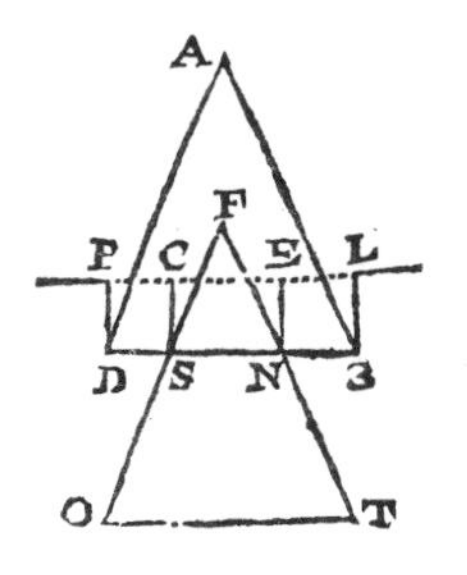

COROLARY I.

I ſay farther; that much leſſe ſhall the ſaid Cone ſtay afloat, if one immerge a part thereof.

Much leſs ſhall the ſaid Cone ſwim, if one immerge a part thereof.

WHich you may ſee, comparing with the water as well the part that ſhall immerge as the other above water. Let us therefore of the Cone A B D, ſubmerge th part N T O S, and advance the Point N S F above water. The Altitude of the Cone F N S, ſhall either be more than half the whole Altitude of the Cone F T O, or it ſhall not be more: if it ſhall be more than half, the Cone F N S ſhall be more than half of the Cylinder E N S C: for the Altitude of the Cone F N S, ſhall be more than Seſquialter of the Altitude of the Cylinder E N S C: And, becauſe the Matter of the Cone is ſuppoſed to be double in Specificall Gravity to the water, the water which would be contained within the Rampart E N S C, would be leſs grave abſolutely than the Cone F N S; ſo that the whole Cone F N S cannot be ſuſtained by the Rampart: But the part immerged N T O S, by being double in Specificall Gravity to the water, ſhall

tend

tend to the bottom: Therefore, the whole Cone F T O, as well in respect of the part submerged, as the part above water shall descend to the bottom. But if the Altitude of the Point F N S, shall be half the Altitude of the whole Cone F T O, the same Altitude of the said Cone F N S shall be Sesquialter to the Altitude E N: and, therefore, E N S C shall be double to the Cone F N S; and as much water in Mass as the Cylinder E N S C, would weigh as much as the part of the Cone F N S. But, because the other immerged part N T O S, is double in Gravity to the water, a Mass of water equall to that compounded of the Cylinder E N S C, and of the Solid N T O S, shall weigh less than the Cone F T O, by as much as the weight of a Mass of water equall to the Solid N T O S: Therefore, the Cone shall also descend. Again, because the Solid N T O S, is septuple to the Cone F N S, to which the Cylinder E S is double, the proportion of the Solid N T O S, shall be to the Cylinder E N S C, as seaven to two: Therefore, the whole Solid compounded of the Cylinder E N S C, and of the Solid N T O S, is much less than double the Solid N T O S: Therefore, the single Solid N T O S, is much graver than a Mass of water equall to the Mass, compounded of the Cylinder E N S C, and of N T O S.

COROLARY II.

Part of the Cones towards the Cuspis removed, it shall still sink.

From whence it followeth, that though one should remove and take away the part of the Cone F N S, the sole remainder N T O S would go to the bottom.

COROLARY III.

The more the Cone is immerged, the more impossible is its floating.

And if we should more depress the Cone F T O, it would be so much the more impossible that it should sustain it self afloat, the part submerged N T O S still encreasing, and the Mass of Air contained in the Rampart diminishing, which ever grows less, the more the Cone submergeth.

THat Cone, therefore, that with its Base upwards, and its *Cuspis* downwards doth swimme, being dimitted with its Base downward must of necessity sinke. They have argued farre from the truth, therefore, who have ascribed the cause of Natation to waters resistance of Division, as to a passive principle, and to the breadth of the Figure, with which the division is to be made, as the Efficient.

I come in the fourth place, to collect and conclude the reason of that which I have proposed to the Adversaries, namely,

THEO-

THEOREME XII.

That it is possible to fo m Solid Bodies, of what Figure and greatness soever, that of their own Nature goe to the Bottome; But by the help of the Air contained in the Rampart, rest without submerging.

Solids of any Figure & greatnesse, that naturally sink, may by help of the Air in the Rampart swimme.

THe truth of this Proposition is sufficiently manifest in all those Solid Figures, that determine in their uppermost part in a plane Superficies: for making such Figures of some Matter specifically as grave as the water, putting them into the water, so that the whole Mass be covered, it is manifest, that they shall rest in all places, provided, that such a Matter equall in weight to the water, may be exactly adjusted: and they shall by consequence, rest or lie even with the Levell of the water, without making any Rampart. If, therefore, in respect of the Matter, such Figures are apt to rest without submerging, though deprived of the help of the Rampart, it is manifest, that they may admit so much encrease of Gravity, (without encreasing their Masses) as is the weight of as much water as would be contained within the Rampart, that is made about their upper plane Surface: by the help of which being sustained, they shall rest afloat, but being bathed, they shall descend, having been made graver than the water. In Figures, therefore, that determine above in a plane, we may cleerly comprehend, that the Rampart added or removed, may prohibit or permit the descent: but in those Figures that go lessening upwards towards the top, some Persons may, and that not without much seeming Reason, doubt whether the same may be done, and especially by those which terminate in a very acute Point, such as are your Cones and small Piramids. Touching these, therefore, as more dubious than the rest, I will endeavour to demonstrate, that they also lie under the same Accident of going, or not going to the Bottom, be they of any whatever bigness. Let therefore the Cone be ABD, made of a matter specifically as grave as the water; it is manifest that being put all under water, it shall rest in all places (alwayes provided, that it shall weigh exactly as much as the water, which is almost impossible to effect) and that any small weight being added to it, it shall sink to the bottom: but if it shall descend downwards gently, I say, that it shall make the Rampart ESTO, and that there shall stay out of the water the point AST, tripple in height to the Rampart ES: which is manifest, for the Matter of the

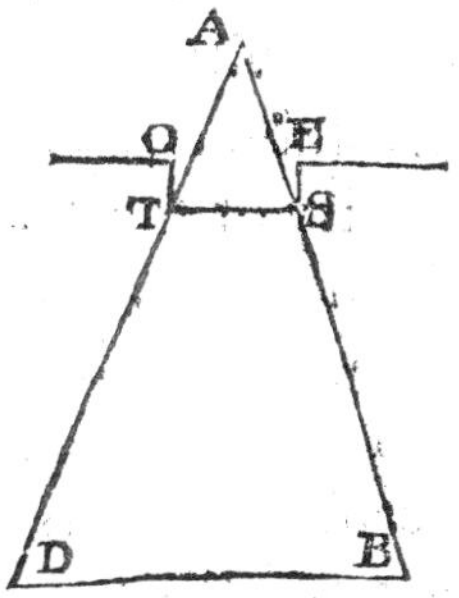

Cone

Cone weighing equally with the water, the part submerged *S B D T*, becomes indifferent to move downwards or upwards; and the Cone *A S T*, being equall in Mass to the water that would be contained in the concave of the Rampart *E S T O*, shall be also equall unto it in Gravity: and, therefore, there shall be a perfect *Equilibrium*, and, consequently, a Rest. Now here ariseth a doubt, whether the Cone *A B D* may be made heavier, in such sort, that when it is put wholly under water, it goes to the bottom, but yet not in such sort, as to take from the Rampart the vertue of sustaining it that it sink not, and, the reason of the doubt is this: that although at such time as the Cone *A B D* is specifically as grave as the water, the Rampart *E S T O* sustaines it, not only when the point *A S T* is tripple in height to the Altitude of the Rampart *E S*, but also when a lesser part is above water; [for although in the Descent of the Cone the Point *A S T* by little and little diminisheth, and so likewise the Rampart *E S T O*, yet the Point diminisheth in greater proportion than the Rampart, in that it diminisheth according to all the three Dimensions, but the Rampart according to two only, the Altitude still remaining the same; or, if you will, because the Cone *S T* goes diminishing, according to the proportion of the cubes of the Lines that do successively become the Diameters of the Bases of emergent Cones, and the Ramparts diminish according to the proportion of the Squares of the same Lines; whereupon the proportions of the Points are alwayes Sesquialter of the proportions of the Cylinders, contained within the Rampart; so that if, for Example, the height of the emergent Point were double, or equall to the height of the Rampart, in these cases, the Cylinder contained within the Rampart, would be much greater than the said Point, because it would be either sesquialter or tripple, by reason of which it would perhaps serve over and above to sustain the whole Cone, since the part submerged would no longer weigh any thing;] yet, neverthelesse, when any Gravity is added to the whole Mass of the Cone, so that also the part submerged is not without some excesse of Gravity above the Gravity of the water, it is not manifest, whether the Cylinder contained within the Rampart, in the descent that the Cone shall make, can be reduced to such a proportion unto the emergent Point, and to such an excesse of Mass above the Mass of it, as to compensate the excesse of the Cones Specificall Gravity above the Gravity of the water: and the Scruple ariseth, because that howbeit in the descent made by the Cone, the emergent Point *A S T* diminisheth, whereby there is also a diminution of the excess of the Cones Gravity above

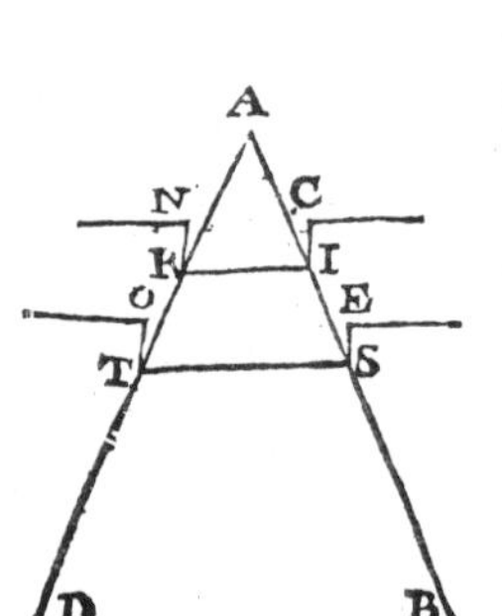

the

the Gravity of the water, yet the case stands so, that the Rampart doth also contract it self, and the Cylinder contained in it doth deminish. Neverthelefs it shall be demonstrated, how that the Cone *A B D* being of any supposed bignesse, and made at the first of a Matter exactly equall in Gravity to the Water, if there may be affixed to it some Weight, by means of which it may descend to the bottom, when submerged under water, it may also by vertue of the Rampart stay above without sinking.

Let, therefore, the Cone *A B D* be of any supposed greatnesse, and alike in specificall Gravity to the water. It is manifest, that being put lightly into the water, it shall rest without descending; and it shall advance above water, the Point *AS T*, tripple in height to the height of the Rampart *E S*: Now, suppose the Cone *A B D* more depressed, so that it advance above water, only the Point *A I R*, higher by half than the Point *A S T*, with the Rampart about it *CIR N*. And, because, the Cone *A B D* is to the Cone *A I R*, as the cube of the Line *S T* is to the cube of the Line *I R*, but the Cylinder *E S T O*, is to the Cylinder *C I R N*, as the Square of *S T* to the Square of *I R*, the Cone *A S T* shall be Octuple to the Cone *A I R*, and the Cylinder *E S T O*, quadruple to the Cylinder *C I R N*: But the Cone *A S T*, is equall to the Cylinder E *S T O* : Therefore, the Cylinder *C I R N*, shall be double to the Cone *A I R* : and the water which might be contained in the Rampart *C I R N*, would be double in Mass and in Weight to the Cone *A I R*, and, therefore, would be able to sustain the double of the Weight of the Cone *AIR*: Therefore, if to the whole Cone *A B D*, there be added as much Weight as the Gravity of the Cone *A I R*, that is to say, the eighth part of the weight of the Cone *A S T*, it also shall be sustained by the Rampart *C I R N*, but without that it shall go to the bottome: the Cone *A B D*, being, by the addition of the eighth part of the weight of the Cone *A S T*, made specifically more grave than the water. But if the Altitude of the Cone *A I R*, were two thirds of the Altitude of the Cone *A S T*, the Cone *A S T* would be to the Cone *A I R*, as twenty seven to eight; and the Cylinder *E S T O*, to the Cylinder *C I R N*, as nine to four, that is, as twenty seven to twelve; and, therefore, the Cylinder *C I R N*, to the Cone *A I R*, as twelve to eight; and the excess of the Cylinder *C I R N*, above the Cone *A I R*, to the Cone *A S T*, as four to twenty seven: therefore if to the Cone *A B D* be added so much weight as is the four twenty sevenths of the weight of the Cone *A S T*, which is a little more then its seventh part, it also shall continue to swimme, and

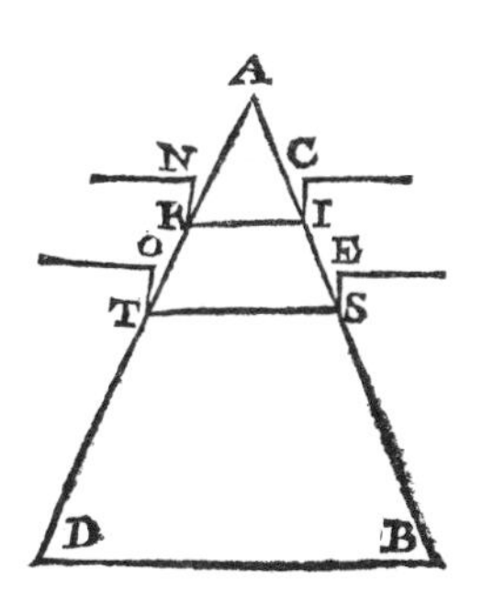

the height of the emergent Point ſhall be double to the height of the Rampart. This that hath been demonſtrated in Cones, exactly holds in Piramides, although the one or the other ſhould be very ſharp in their Point or Cuſpis: From whence we conclude, that the ſame Accident ſhall ſo much the more eaſily happen in all other Figures, by how much the leſs ſharp the Tops ſhall be, in which they determine, being aſſiſted by more ſpacious Ramparts.

Natation eaſieſt effected in Figures broad toward the top.

THEOREME XIII.

All Figures, therefore, of whatever greatneſſe, may go, and not go, to the Bottom, according as their Summities or Tops ſhall be bathed or not bathed.

All Figures ſink or ſwim, upon bathing or not bathing of their tops.

AND this Accident being common to all ſorts of Figures, without exception of ſo much as one. Figure hath, therefore, no part in the production of this Effect, of ſometimes ſinking, and ſometimes again not ſinking, but only the being ſometimes conjoyned to, and ſometimes ſeperated from, the ſupereminent Air: which cauſe, in fine, who ſo ſhall rightly, and, as we ſay, with both his Eyes, conſider this buſineſs, will find that it is reduced to, yea, that it really is the ſame with, the true, Naturall and primary cauſe of Natation or Submerſion; to wit, the exceſs or deficiency of the Gravity of the water, in relation to the Gravity of that Solid Magnitude, that is demitted into the water. For like as a Plate of Lead, as thick as the back of a Knife, which being put into the water by it ſelf alone goes to the bottom, if upon it you faſten a piece of Cork four fingers thick, doth continue afloat, for that now the Solid that is demitted in the water, is not, as before, more grave than the water, but leſs, ſo the Board of Ebony, of its own nature more grave than water; and, therefore, deſcending to the bottom, when it is demitted by it ſelf alone into the water, if it ſhall be put upon the water, conjoyned with an Expanded vail of Air, that together with the Ebony doth deſcend, and that it be ſuch, as that it doth make with it a compound leſs grave than ſo much water in Maſs, as equalleth the Maſs already ſubmerged and depreſſed beneath the Levell of the waters Surface, it ſhall not deſcend any farther, but ſhall reſt, for no other than the univerſall and moſt common cauſe, which is that Solid Magnitudes, leſs grave *in ſpecie* than the water, go not to the bottom.

So that if one ſhould take a Plate of Lead, as for Example, a finger thick, and an handfull broad every way, and ſhould attempt to make it ſwimme, with putting it lightly on the water, he would loſe his Labour, becauſe that if it ſhould be depreſſed an Hairs breadth beyond

yond the possible Altitude of the Ramparts of water, it would dive and sink; but if whilst it is going downwards, one should make certain Banks or Ramparts about it, that should hinder the defusion of the water upon the said Plate, the which Banks should rise so high, as that they might be able to contain as much water, as should weigh equally with the said Plate, it would, without all Question, descend no lower, but would rest, as being sustained by vertue of the Air contained within the aforesaid Ramparts: and, in short, there would be a Vessell by this means formed with the bottom of Lead. But if the thinness of the Lead shall be such, that a very small height of Rampart would suffice to contain so much Air, as might keep it afloat, it shall also rest without the Artificiall Banks or Ramparts, but yet not without the Air, because the Air by it self makes Banks sufficient for a small height, to resist the Superfusion of the water: so that that which in this case swimmes, is as it were a Vessell filled with Air, by vertue of which it continueth afloat.

I will, in the last place, with an other Experiment, attempt to remove all difficulties, if so be there should yet be any doubt left in any one, touching the opperation of this *Continuity of the Air, with the thin Plate which swims, and afterwards put an end to this part of my discourse.

*Or rather Contiguity,

I suppose my self to be questioning with some of my Oponents.

Whether Figure have any influence upon the encrease or diminution of the Resistance in any Weight against its being raised in the Air; and I suppose, that I am to maintain the Affirmative, asserting that a Mass of Lead, reduced to the Figure of a Ball, shall be raised with less force, then if the same had been made into a thinne and broad Plate, because that it in this spacious Figure, hath a great quantity of Air to penetrate, and in that other, more compacted and contracted very little: and to demonstrate the truth of such my Opinion, I will hang in a small thred first the Ball or Bullet, and put that into the water, tying the thred that upholds it to one end of the Ballance that I hold in the Air, and to the other end I by degrees adde so much Weight, till that at last it brings up the Ball of Lead out of the water: to do which, suppose a Gravity of thirty Ounces sufficeth; I afterwards reduce the said Lead into a flat and thinne Plate, the which I likewise put into the water, suspended by three threds, which hold it parallel to the Surface of the water, and putting in the same manner, Weights to the other end, till such time as the Plate comes to be raised and drawn out of the water: I finde that thirty six ounces will not suffice to seperate it from the water, and raise it thorow the Air: and arguing from this Experiment, I affirm, that I have fully demonstrated the truth of my Proposition. Here my Oponents desires me to look down, shewing me a thing

An Experiment of the operation of Figures, in encreasing or lessening of the Airs Resistance of Division.

which I had not before obſerved, to wit, that in the Aſcent of the Plate out of the water, it draws after it another Plate (*if I may ſo call it*) of water, which before it divides and parts from the inferiour Surface of the Plate of Lead, is raiſed above the Levell of the other water, more than the thickneſs of the back of a Knife: Then he goeth to repeat the Experiment with the Ball, and makes me ſee, that it is but a very ſmall quantity of water, which cleaves to its compacted and contracted Figure: and then he ſubjoynes, that its no wonder, if in ſeperating the thinne and broad Plate from the water, we meet with much greater Reſiſtance, than in ſeperating the Ball, ſince together with the Plate, we are to raiſe a great quantity of water, which occurreth not in the Ball: He telleth me moreover, how that our Queſtion is, whether the Reſiſtance of Elevation be greater in a dilated Plate of Lead, than in a Ball, and not whether more reſiſteth a Plate of Lead with a great quantity of water, or a Ball with a very little water: He ſheweth me in the cloſe, that the putting the Plate and the Ball firſt into the water, to make proofe thereby of their Reſiſtance in the Air, is beſides our caſe, which treats of Elivating in the Air, and of things placed in the Air, and not of the Reſiſtance that is made in the Confines of the Air and water, and by things which are part in Air and part in water: and laſtly, they make me feel with my hand, that when the thinne Plate is in the Air, and free from the weight of the water, it is raiſed with the very ſame Force that raiſeth the Ball. Seeing, and underſtanding theſe things, I know not what to do, unleſs to grant my ſelf convinced, and to thank ſuch a Friend, for having made me to ſee that which I never till then obſerved: and, being advertiſed by this ſame Accident, to tell my Adverſaries, that our Queſtion is, whether a Board and a Ball of Ebony, equally go to the bottom in water, and not a Ball of Ebony and a Board of Ebony, joyned with another flat Body of Air: and, farthermore, that we ſpeak of ſinking, and not ſinking to the bottom, in water, and not of that which happeneth in the Confines of the water and Air to Bodies that be part in the Air, and part in the water; nor much leſs do we treat of the greater or leſſer Force requiſite in ſeperating this or that Body from the Air; not omitting to tell them, in the laſt place, that the Air doth reſiſt, and gravitate downwards in the water, juſt ſo much as the water (if I may ſo ſpeak) gravitates and reſiſts upwards in the Air, and that the ſame Force is required to ſinke a Bladder under water, that is full of Air, as to raiſe it in the Air, being full of water, removing the conſideration of the weight of that Filme or Skinne, and conſidering the water and the Air only. And it is likewiſe true, that the ſame Force is required to ſink a Cup or ſuch like Veſſell under water, whilſt it is full of Air, as to raiſe it above the Superficies of the water, keeping

it

it with the mouth downwards; whilst it is full of water, which is constrained in the same manner to follow the Cup which contains it, and to rise above the other water into the Region of the Air, as the Air is forced to follow the same Vessell under the Surface of the water, till that in this case the water, surmounting the brimme of the Cup, breaks in, driving thence the Air, and in that case, the said brimme coming out of the water, and arriving to the Confines of the Air, the water falls down, and the Air sub-enters to fill the cavity of the Cup: upon which ensues, that he no less transgresses the Articles of the *Convention*, who produceth a Plate conjoyned with much Air, to see if it descend to the bottom in water, then he that makes proof of the Resistance against Elevation in Air with a Plate of Lead, joyned with a like quantity of water.

Aristotles opinion touching the Operation of Figure examined.

Aristot. de Cælo, Lib. 4. Cap. 6.

I have said all that I could at present think of, to maintain the Assertion I have undertook. It remains, that I examine that which *Aristotle* hath writ of this matter towards the end of his Book *De Cælo*; wherein I shall note two things: the one that it being true as hath been demonstrated, that Figure hath nothing to do about the moving or not moving it self upwards or downwards, it seemes that *Aristotle* at his first falling upon this Speculation, was of the same opinion, as in my opinion may be collected from the examination of his words. 'Tis true, indeed, that in essaying afterwards to render a reason of such effect, as not having in my conceit hit upon the right, (which in the second place I will examine) it seems that he is brought to admit the largenesse of Figure, to be interessed in this operation. As to the first particuler, hear the precise words of *Aristotle*.

Aristotle makes not Figure the cause of Motion absolutely, but of swift or slow motion,

Lib. 4. Cap. 6. Text. 42.

Figures are not the Causes of moving simply upwards or downwards, but of moving more slowly or swiftly, and by what means this comes to pass, it is not difficult to see.

Here first I note, that the terms being four, which fall under the present consideration, namely, Motion, Rest, Slowly and Swiftly: And *Aristotle* naming Figures as Causes of Tardity and Velocity, excluding them from being the Cause of absolute and simple Motion, it seems necessary, that he exclude them on the other side, from being the Cause of Rest, so that his meaning is this. Figures are not the Causes of moving or not moving absolutely, but of moving quickly or slowly: and, here, if any should say the mind of *Aristotle* is to exclude Figures from being Causes of Motion, but yet not from being Causes of Rest, so that the sence would be to remove from Figures, there being the Causes of moving simply, but yet not there being Causes of Rest, I would demand, whether we ought with *Aristotle* to understand, that all Figures universally, are, in some manner, the causes of Rest in those Bodies, which otherwise would move, or else some particular Figures only, as for Example, broad

and

and thinne Figures : If all indifferently, then every Body ſhall reſt : becauſe every Body hath ſome Figure, which is falſe : but if ſome particular Figures only may be in ſome manner a Cauſe of Reſt, as, for Example, the broad, then the others would be in ſome manner the Cauſes of Motion : for if from ſeeing ſome Bodies of a contracted Figure move, which after dilated into Plates reſt, may be inferred, that the Amplitude of Figure hath a part in the Cauſe of that Reſt; ſo from ſeeing ſuch like Figures reſt, which afterwards contracted move, it may with the ſame reaſon be affirmed, that the united and contracted Figure, hath a part in cauſing Motion, as the remover of that which impeded it : The which again is directly oppoſite to what *Ariſtotle* ſaith, namely, that Figures are not the Cauſes of Motion. Beſides, if *Ariſtotle* had admitted and not excluded Figures from being Cauſes of not moving in ſome Bodies, which moulded into another Figure would move, he would have impertinently propounded in a dubitative manner, in the words immediately following, whence it is, that the large and thinne Plates of Lead or Iron, reſt upon the water, ſince the Cauſe was apparent, namely, the Amplitude of Figure. Let us conclude, therefore, that the meaning of *Ariſtotle* in this place is to affirm, that Figures are not the Cauſes of abſolutely moving or not moving, but only of moving ſwiftly or ſlowly : which we ought the rather to believe, in regard it is indeed a moſt true conceipt and opinion. Now the mind of *Ariſtotle* being ſuch, and appearing by conſequence, rather contrary at the firſt ſight, then favourable to the aſſertion of the Oponents, it is neceſſary, that their Interpretation be not exactly the ſame with that, but ſuch, as being in part underſtood by ſome of them, and in part by others, was ſet down : and it may eaſily be indeed ſo, being an Interpretation conſonent to the ſence of the more famous Interpretors, which is, that the Adverbe *Simply* or *Abſolutely*, put in the Text, ought not to be joyned to the Verbe to *Move*, but with the Noun *Cauſes* : ſo that the purport of *Ariſtotles* words, is to affirm, That Figures are not the Cauſes abſolutely of moving or not moving, but yet are Cauſes *Secundum quid*, *viz.* in ſome ſort ; by which means, they are called Auxiliary and Concomitant Cauſes : and this Propoſition is received and aſſerted as true by *Signor Buonamico Lib.* 5. *Cap.* 28. where he thus writes. *There are other Cauſes concomitant, by which ſome things float, and others ſink, among which the Figures of Bodies hath the firſt place*, &c.

Concerning this Propoſition, I meet with many doubts and difficulties, for which me thinks the words of *Ariſtotle* are not capable of ſuch a conſtruction and ſence, and the difficulties are theſe.

Firſt in the order and diſpoſure of the words of *Ariſtotle*, the particle *Simpliciter*, or if you will *abſolutè*, is conjoyned with the Verb

to

to move, and seperated from the Noun *Causes*, the which is a great presumption in my favour, seeing that the writing and the Text saith, Figures are not the Cause of moving simply upwards or downwards, but of quicker or slower Motion : and, saith not, Figures are not simply the Causes of moving upwards or downwards, and when the words of a Text receive, transposed, a sence different from that which they sound, taken in the order wherein the Author disposeth them, it is not convenient to inverte them. And who will affirm that *Aristotle* desiring to write a Proposition, would dispose the words in such sort, that they should import a different, nay, a contrary sence? contrary, I say, because understood as they are written; they say, that Figures are not the Causes of Motion, but inverted, they say, that Figures are the Causes of Motion, &c.

Moreover, if the intent of *Aristotle* had been to say, that Figures are not simply the Causes of moving upwards or downwards, but only Causes *Secundum quid*, he would not have adjoyned those words, *but they are Causes of the more swift or slow Motion*; yea, the subjoining this would have been not only superfluous but false, for that the whole tenour of the Proposition would import thus much. Figures are not the absolute Causes of moving upwards or downwards, but are the absolute Cause of the swift or slow Motion; which is not true : because the primary Causes of greater or lesser Velocity, are by *Aristotle* in the 4th of his *Physicks*, *Text.* 71. attributed to the greater or lesser Gravity of Moveables, compared among themselves, and to the greater or lesser Resistance of the *Medium's*, depending on their greater or less Crassitude : and these are inserted by *Aristotle* as the primary Causes; and these two only are in that place nominated : and Figure comes afterwards to be considered, *Text.* 74. rather as an Instrumentall Cause of the force of the Gravity, the which divides either with the Figure, or with the *Impetus*; and, indeed, Figure by it self without the force of Gravity or Levity, would opperate nothing.

I adde, that if *Aristotle* had an opinion that Figure had been in some sort the Cause of moving or not moving, the inquisition which he makes immediately in a doubtfull manner, whence it comes, that a Plate of Lead flotes, would have been impertinent; for if but just before he had said, that Figure was in a certain sort the Cause of moving or not moving, he needed not to call in Question, by what Cause the Plate of Lead swims, and then ascribing the Cause to its Figure; and framing a discourse in this manner. Figure is a Cause *Secundum quid* of not sinking : but, now, if it be doubted, for what Cause a thin Plate of Lead goes not to the bottom; it shall be answered, that that proceeds from its Figure : a discourse which

which would be indecent in a Child, much more in *Ariſtotle*; For where is the occaſion of doubting? And who ſees not, that if *Ariſtotle* had held, that Figure was in ſome ſort a Cauſe of Natation, he would without the leaſt Heſitation have writ; That Figure is in a certain ſort the Cauſe of Natation, and therefore the Plate of Lead in reſpect of its large and expatiated Figure ſwims; but if we take the propoſition of *Ariſtotle* as I ſay, and as it is written, and as indeed it is true, the enſuing words come in very oppoſitely, as well in the introduction of ſwift and ſlow, as in the queſtion, which very pertinently offers it ſelf, and would ſay thus much.

Figures are not the Cauſe of moving or not moving ſimply upwards or downwards, but of moving more quickly or ſlowly: But if it be ſo, the Cauſe is doubtfull, whence it proceeds, that a Plate of Lead or of Iron broad and thin doth ſwim, &c. And the occaſion of the doubt is obvious, becauſe it ſeems at the firſt glance, that the Figure is the Cauſe of this Natation, ſince the ſame Lead, or a leſs quantity, but in another Figure, goes to the bottom, and we have already affirmed, that the Figure hath no ſhare in this effect.

Laſtly, if the intent of *Ariſtotle* in this place had been to ſay, that Figures, although not abſolutely, are at leaſt in ſome meaſure the Cauſe of moving or not moving: I would have it conſidered, that he names no leſs the Motion upwards, than the other downwards: and becauſe in exemplifying it afterwards, he produceth no other Experiments than of a Plate of Lead, and Board of Ebony, Matters that of their own Nature go to the bottom, but by vertue (as our Adverſaries ſay) of their Figure, reſt afloat; it is fit that they ſhould produce ſome other Experiment of thoſe Matters, which by their Nature ſwims, but retained by their Figure reſt at the bottom. But ſince this is impoſſible to be done, we conclude, that *Ariſtotle* in this place, hath not attributed any action to the Figure of ſimply moving or not moving.

But though he hath exquiſitely Philoſophiz'd, in inveſtigating the ſolution of the doubts he propoſeth, yet will I not undertake to maintain, rather various difficulties, that preſent themſelves unto me, give me occaſion of ſuſpecting that he hath not entirely diſplaid unto us, the true Cauſe of the preſent Concluſion: which difficulties I will propound one by one, ready to change opinion, when ever I am ſhewed, that the Truth is different from what I ſay; to the confeſſion whereof I am much more inclinable than to contradiction.

Ariſtotle erred in affirming a Needle dimitted long wayes to ſink.

Ariſtotle having propounded the Queſtion, whence it proceeds, that broad Plates of Iron or Lead, float or ſwim; he addeth (as it were ſtrengthening the occaſion of doubting) foraſmuch as other things, leſs, and leſs grave, be they round or long, as for inſtance a

Needle

Needle go to the bottom. Now I here doubt, or rather am certain, that a Needle put lightly upon the water, rests afloat, no less than the thin Plates of Iron or Lead. I cannot believe, albeit it hath been told me, that some to defend *Aristotle* should say, that he intends a Needle demitted not longwayes but endwayes, and with the Point downwards; neverthelefs, not to leave them so much as this, though very weak refuge, and which in my judgement *Aristotle* himself would refuse, I say it ought to be understood, that the Needle must be demitted, according to the Dimension named by *Aristotle*, which is the length : because, if any other Dimension than that which is named, might or ought to be taken, I would say, that even the Plates of Iron and Lead, sink to the bottom, if they be put into the water edgewayes and not flatwayes. But because *Aristotle* saith, broad Figures go not to the bottom, it is to be understood, being demitted broadwayes : and, therefore, when he saith, long Figures as a Needle, albeit light, rest not afloat, it ought to be understood of them when demitted longwayes.

Moreover, to say that Aristotle *is to be understood of the Needle demitted with the Point downwards, is to father upon him a great impertinency; for in this place he saith, that little Particles of Lead or Iron, if they be round or long as a Needle, do sink to the bottome; so that by his Opinion, a Particle or small Grain of Iron cannot swim : and if he thus believed, what a great folly would it be to subjoyn, that neither would a Needle demitted endwayes swim? And what other is such a Needle, but many such like Graines accumulated one upon another? It was too unworthy of such a man to say, that one single Grain of Iron could not swim, and that neither can it swim, though you put a hundred more upon it.*

Lastly, either *Aristotle* believed, that a Needle demitted longwayes upon the water, would swim, or he believed that it would not swim : If he believed it would not swim, he might well speak as indeed he did; but if he believed and knew that it would float, why, together with the dubious Problem of the Natation of broad Figures, though of ponderous Matter, hath he not also introduced the Question; whence it proceeds, that even long and slender Figures, howbeit of Iron or Lead do swim? And the rather, for that the occasion of doubting seems greater in long and narrow Figures, than in broad and thin, as from *Aristotles* not having doubted of it, is manifested.

No lesser an inconvenience would they fasten upon *Aristotle*, who in his defence should say, that he means a Needle pretty thick, and not a small one; for take it for granted to be intended of a small one;

and it shall suffice to reply, that he believed that it would swim; and I will again charge him with having avoided a more wonderfull and intricate Probleme, and introduced the more facile and less wonderfull.

We say freely therefore, that *Aristotle* did hold, that only the broad Figure did swim, but the long and slender, such as a Needle, not. The which neverthelesse is false, as it is also false in round Bodies: because, as from what hath been predemonstrated, may be gathered, little Balls of Lead and Iron, do in like manner swim.

Aristotle affirmeth some Bodies volatile for their Minuity, Text. 42.

He proposeth likewise another Conclusion, which likewise seems different from the truth, and it is, That some things, by reason of their littlenesse fly in the Air, as the small dust of the Earth, and the thin leaves of beaten Gold : but in my Opinion, Experience shews us, that that happens not only in the Air, but also in the water, in which do descend, even those Particles or Atomes of Earth, that disturbe it, whose minuity is such, that they are not deservable, save only when they are many hundreds together. Therefore, the dust of the Earth, and beaten Gold, do not any way sustain themselves in the Air, but descend downwards, and only fly to and again in the same, when strong Windes raise them, or other agitations of the Air commove them : and this also happens in the commotion of the water, which raiseth its Sand from the bottom, and makes it muddy. But *Aristotle* cannot mean this impediment of the commotion, of which he makes no mention, nor names other than the lightnesse of such Minutiæ or Atomes, and the Resistance of the Crassitudes of the Water and Air, by which we see, that he speakes of a calme, and not disturbed and agitated Air : but in that case, neither Gold nor Earth, be they never so small, are sustained, but speedily descend.

Democritus placed the Cause of Natation in certain fiery Atomes.

Aristot. De Cœlo lib. 4. cap. 6. text. 43.

He passeth next to confute *Democritus*, which, by his Testimony would have it, that some Fiery Atomes, which continually ascend through the water, do spring upwards, and sustain those grave Bodies, which are very broad, and that the narrow descend to the bottom, for that but a small quantity of those Atomes, encounter and resist them.

Democritus confuted by *Aristotle*, text 43.

Aristotles confutation of *Democritus* refuted by the Author.

I say, *Aristotle* confutes this position, saying, that that should much more occurre in the Air, as the same *Democritus* instances against himself, but after he had moved the objection, he slightly resolves it, with saying, that those Corpuscles which ascend in the Air, make not their *Impetus* conjunctly. Here I will not say, that the reason alledged by *Democritus* is true, but I will only say, it seems in my judgement, that it is not wholly confuted by *Aristotle*, whilst he saith, that were it true, that the calid ascending Atomes, should sustain Bodies grave, but very broad, it would much more be done in the Air, than in Water, for that haply in the Opinion of *Aristotle*,

the

the said calid Atomes ascend with much greater Force and Velocity through the Air, than through the water. And if this be so, as I verily believe it is, the Objection of *Aristotle* in my judgement seems to give occasion of suspecting, that he may possibly be deceived in more than one particular: First, because those calid Atomes, (whether they be Fiery Corpuscles, or whether they be Exhalations, or in short, whatever other matter they be, that ascends upwards through the Air) cannot be believed to mount faster through Air, than through water: but rather on the contrary, they peradventure move more impetuously through the water, than through the Air, as hath been in part demonstrated above. And here I cannot finde the reason, why *Aristotle* seeing, that the descending Motion of the same Moveable, is more swift in Air, than in water, hath not advertised us, that from the contrary Motion, the contrary should necessarily follow; to wit, that it is more swift in the water, than in the Air: for since that the Moveable which descendeth, moves swifter through the Air, than through the water, if we should suppose its Gravity gradually to diminish, it would first become such, that descending swiftly through the Air, it would descend but slowly through the water: and then again, it might be such, that descending in the Air, it should ascend in the water: and being made yet less grave, it shall ascend swiftly through the water, and yet descend likewise through the Air: and in short, before it can begin to ascend, though but slowly through the Air, it shall ascend swiftly through the water: how then is it true, that ascending Moveables move swifter through the Air, than through the water?

That which hath made *Aristotle* believe, the Motion of Ascent to be swifter in Air, than in water, was first, the having referred the Causes of slow and quick, as well in the Motion of Ascent, as of Descent, only to the diversity of the Figures of the Moveable, and to the more or less Resistance of the greater or lesser Crassitude, or Rarity of the *Medium*; not regarding the comparison of the Excesses of the Gravities of the Moveables, and of the *Mediums*: the which notwithstanding, is the most principal point in this affair: for if the augmentation and diminution of the Tardity or Velocity, should have only respect to the Density or Rarity of the *Medium*, every Body that descends in Air, would descend in water: because whatever difference is found between the Crassitude of the water, and that of the Air, may well be found between the Velocity of the same Moveable in the Air, and some other Velocity: and this should be its proper Velocity in the water, which is absolutely false. The other occasion is, that he did believe, that like as there is a positive and intrinsecall Quality, whereby Elementary Bodies have a propension of moving towards the Centre of the Earth, so there is another like-

Lib. 4. Cap. 5.

wise intrinsecall, whereby some of those Bodies have an *Impetus* of flying the Centre, and moving upwards : by Vertue of which intrinsecall Principle, called by him Levity, the Moveables which have that same Motion more easily penetrate the more subtle *Medium*, than the more dense : but such a Proposition appears likewise uncertain, as I have above hinted in part, and as with Reasons and Experiments, I could demonstrate, did not the present Argument importune me, or could I dispatch it in few words.

The Objection therefore of *Aristotle* against *Democritus*, whilst he saith, that if the Fiery ascending Atomes should sustain Bodies grave, but of a distended Figure, it would be more observable in the Air than in the water, because such Corpuscles move swifter in that, than in this, is not good; yea the contrary would evene, for that they ascend more slowly through the Air : and, besides their moving slowly, they ascend, not united together, as in the water, but discontinue, and, as we say, scatter : And, therefore, as *Democritus* well replyes, resolving the instance they make not their push or *Impetus* conjunctly.

Aristotle, in the second place, deceives himself, whilst he will have the said grave Bodies to be more easily sustained by the said Fiery ascending Atomes in the Air than in the Water : not observing, that the said Bodies are much more grave in that, than in this, and that such a Body weighs ten pounds in the Air, which will not in the water weigh ½ an ounce ; how can it then be more easily sustained in the Air, than in the Water?

Democritus confuted by the Authour.

Let us conclude, therefore, that *Democritus* hath in this particular better Philosophated than *Aristotle*. But yet will not I affirm, that *Democritus* hath reason'd rightly, but I rather say, that there is a manifest Experiment that overthrows his Reason, and this it is, That if it were true, that calid ascending Atomes should uphold a Body, that if they did not hinder, would go to the bottom, it would follow, that we may find a Matter very little superiour in Gravity to the water, the which being reduced into a Ball, or other contracted Figure, should go to the bottom, as encountring but few Fiery Atomes; and which being distended afterwards into a dilated and thin Plate, should come to be thrust upwards by the impulsion of a great Multitude of those Corpuscles, and at last carried to the very Surface of the water : which wee see not to happen; Experience shewing us, that a Body *v. gra.* of a Sphericall Figure, which very hardly, and with very great leasure goeth to the bottom, will rest there, and will also descend thither, being reduced into whatsoever other distended Figure. We must needs say then, either that in the water, there are no such ascending Fiery Atoms, or if that such there be, that they are not able to raise and lift up any Plate of a Matter,

that

that without them would go to the bottom : Of which two Positions, I esteem the second to be true, understanding it of water, constituted in its naturall Coldness. But if we take a Vessel of Glass, or Brass, or any other hard matter, full of cold water, within which is put a Solid of a flat or concave Figure, but that in Gravity exceeds the water so little, that it goes slowly to the bottom ; I say, that putting some burning Coals under the said Vessel, as soon as the new Fiery Atomes shall have penetrated the substance of the Vessel, they shall without doubt, ascend through that of the water, and thrusting against the foresaid Solid, they shall drive it to the Superficies, and there detain it, as long as the incursions of the said Corpuscles shall last, which ceasing after the removall of the Fire, the Solid being abandoned by its supporters, shall return to the bottom.

But *Democritus* notes, that this Cause only takes place when we treat of raising and sustaining of Plates of Matters, but very little heavier than the water, or extreamly thin : but in Matters very grave, and of some thickness, as Plates of Lead or other Mettal, that same Effect wholly ceaseth : In Testimony of which, let's observe that such Plates, being raised by the Fiery Atomes, ascend through all the depth of the water, and stop at the Confines of the Air, still staying under water : but the Plates of the Opponents stay not, but only when they have their upper Superficies dry, nor is there any means to be used, that when they are within the water, they may not sink to the bottom. The cause, therefore, of the Supernatation of the things of which *Democritus* speaks is one, and that of the Supernatation of the things of which we speak is another. But, returning to *Aristotle*, methinks that he hath more weakly confuted *Democritus*, than *Democritus* himself hath done : For *Aristotle* having propounded the Objection which he maketh against him, and opposed him with saying, that if the calid ascendent Corpuscles were those that raised the thin Plate, much more then would such a Solid be raised and born upwards through the Air, it sheweth that the desire in *Aristotle* to detect *Democritus*, was predominate over the exquisiteness of Solid Philosophizing : which desire of his he hath discovered in other occasions, and that we may not digress too far from this place, in the Text precedent to this Chapter which we have in hand ; where he attempts to confute the same *Democritus*, for that he, not contenting himself with names only, had essayed more particularly to declare what things Gravity and Levity were ; that is, the Causes of descending and ascending, (and had introduced Repletion and Vacuity) ascribing this to Fire, by which it moves upwards, and that to the Earth, by which it descends ; afterwards attributing to the Air more of Fire, and to the water more of Earth. But *Aristotle* desiring a positive Cause, even of ascending Motion, and not as *Plato*, or

Aristotle shews his desire of finding *Democritus* in an Error, to exceed that of discovering Truth.

Cap. 5. Text 41.

or these others, a simple negation, or privation, such as Vacuity would be in reference to Repletion, argueth against *Democritus* and saith : If it be true, as you suppose, then there shall be a great Mass of water, which shall have more of Fire, than a small Mass of Air, and a great Mass of Air, which shall have more of Earth than a little Mass of water, whereby it would ensue, that a great Mass of Air, should come more swiftly downwards, than a little quantity of water : But that is never in any case soever : Therefore *Democritus* discourseth erroneously.

Id.ibid.

But in my opinion, the Doctrine of *Democritus*, is not by this allegation overthrown, but if I erre not, the manner of *Aristotle* deduction either concludes not, or if it do conclude any thing, it may with equall force be restored against himself. *Democritus* will grant to *Aristotle*, that there may be a great Mass of Air taken, which contains more Earth, than a small quantity of water, but yet will deny, that such a Mass of Air, shall go faster downwards than a little water, and that for many reasons. First, because if the greater quantity of Earth, contained in the great Mass of Air, ought to cause a greater Velocity than a less quantity of Earth, contained in a little quantity of water, it would be necessary, first, that it were true, that a greater Mass of pure Earth, should move more swiftly than a less: But this is false, though *Aristotle* in many places affirms it to be true: because not the greater absolute, but the greater specificall Gravity, is the cause of greater Velocity : nor doth a Ball of Wood, weighing ten pounds, descend more swiftly than one weighing ten Ounces, and that is of the same Matter : but indeed a Bullet of Lead of four Ounces, descendeth more swiftly than a Ball of Wood of twenty Pounds : because the Lead is more grave *in specie* than the Wood. Therefore, its not necessary, that a great Mass of Air, by reason of the much Earth contained in it, do descend more swiftly than a little Mass of water, but on the contrary, any whatsoever Mass of water, shall move more swiftly than any other of Air, by reason the participation of the terrene parts *in specie* is greater in the water, than in the Air. Let us note, in the second place, how that in multiplying the Mass of the Air, we not only multiply that which is therein of terrene, but its Fire also : whence the Cause of ascending, no less encreaseth, by vertue of the Fire, than that of descending on the account of its multiplied Earth. It was requisite in increasing the greatness of the Air, to multiply that which it hath of terrene only, leaving its Fire in its first state, for then the terrene parts of the augmented Air, overcoming the terrene parts of the small quantity of water, it might with more probability have been pretended, that the great quantity of Air, ought to descend with a greater *Impetus*, than the little quantity of water.

The greater Specificall, not the greater absolute Gravity, is the Cause of Velocity.

Any Mass of water shal move more swiftly, than any of Air, and why.

Therefore,

Therefore, the Fallacy lyes more in the Discourse of *Aristotle*, than in that of *Democritus*, who with severall other Reasons might oppose *Aristotle*, and alledge; If it be true, that the extreame Elements be one simply grave, and the other simply light, and that the mean Elements participate of the one, and of the other Nature; but the Air more of Levity, and the water more of Gravity, then there shall be a great Mass of Air, whose Gravity shall exceed the Gravity of a little quantity of water, and therefore such a Mass of Air shall descend more swiftly than that little water: But that is never seen to occurr: Therefore its not true, that the mean Elements do participate of the one, and the other quality. This argument is fallacious, no less than the other against *Democritus*.

Lastly, *Aristotle* having said, that if the Position of *Democritus* were true, it would follow, that a great Mass of Air should move more swiftly than a small Mass of water, and afterwards subjoyned, that that is never seen in any Case: methinks others may become desirous to know of him in what place this should evene, which he deduceth against *Democritus*, and what Experiment teacheth us, that it never falls out so. To suppose to see it in the Element of water, or in that of the Air is vain, because neither doth water through water, nor Air through Air move, nor would they ever by any whatever participation others assign them, of Earth or of Fire: the Earth, in that it is not a Body fluid, and yielding to the mobility of other Bodies, is a most improper place and *Medium* for such an Experiment: *Vacuum*, according to the same *Aristotle* himself, there is none, and were there, nothing would move in it: there remains the Region of Fire, but being so far distant from us, what Experiment can assure us, or hath assertained *Aristotle* in such sort, that he should as of a thing most obvious to sence, affirm what he produceth in confutation of *Democritus*, to wit, that a great Mass of Air, is moved no swifter than a little one of water? But I will dwell no longer upon this matter, whereon I have spoke sufficiently: but leaving *Democritus*, I return to the Text of *Aristotle*, wherein he goes about to render the true reason, how it comes to pass, that the thin Plates of Iron or Lead do swim on the water; and, moreover, that Gold it self being beaten into thin Leaves, not only swims in water, but flyeth too and again in the Air. He supposeth that of Continualls, some are easily divisible, others not: and that of the easily divisible, some are more so, and some less: and these he affirms we should esteem the Causes. He addes that that is easily divisible, which is well terminated, and the more the more divisible, and that the Air is more so, than the water, and the water than the Earth. And, lastly, he supposeth that in each kind, the lesse quantity is easlyer divided and broken than the greater.

De Cœlo l. 4. c. 6. t. 44.

Here

Here I note, that the Conclusions of *Aristotle* in generall are all true, but methinks, that he applyeth them to particulars, in which they have no place, as indeed they have in others, as for Example, Wax is more easily divisible than Lead, and Lead than Silver, inasmuch as Wax receives all the terms more easlier than Lead, and Lead than Silver. Its true, moreover, that a little quantity of Silver is easlier divided than a great Mass: and all these Propositions are true, because true it is, that in Silver, Lead and Wax, there is simply a Resistance against Division, and where there is the absolute, there is also the respective. But if as well in water as in Air, there be no Renitence against simple Division, how can we say, that the water is easlier divided than the Air? We know not how to extricate our selves from the Equivocation: whereupon I return to answer, that Resistance of absolute Division is one thing, and Resistance of Division made with such and such Velocity is another. But to produce Rest, and to abate the Motion, the Resistance of absolute Division is necessary; and the Resistance of speedy Division, causeth not Rest, but slowness of Motion. But that as well in the Air, as in water, there is no Resistance of simple Division, is manifest, for that there is not found any Solid Body which divides not the Air, and also the water: and that beaten Gold, or small dust, are not able to superate the Resistance of the Air, is contrary to that which Experience shews us, for we see Gold and Dust to go waving to and again in the Air, and at last to descend downwards, and to do the same in the water, if it be put therein, and separated from the Air. And, because, as I say, neither the water, nor the Air do resist simple Division, it cannot be said, that the water resists more than the Air. Nor let any object unto me, the Example of most light Bodies, as a Feather, or a little of the pith of Elder, or water-reed that divides the Air and not the water, and from this infer, that the Air is easlier divisible than the water; for I say unto them, that if they do well observe, they shall see the same Body likewise divide the Continuity of the water, and submerge in part, and in such a part, as that so much water in Mass would weigh as much as the whole Solid. And if they shal yet persist in their doubt, that such a Solid sinks not through inability to divide the water, I will return them this reply, that if they put it under water, and then let it go, they shall see it divide the water, and presently ascend with no less celerity, than that with which it divided the Air in descending: so that to say that this Solid ascends in the Air, but that coming to the water, it ceaseth its Motion, and therefore the water is more difficult to be divided, concludes nothing: for I, on the contrary, will propose them a piece of Wood, or of Wax, which riseth from the bottom of the water, and easily divides its Resistance, which afterwards being arrived

Archimed. De Insident. humi lib. 2. prop. 1.

ved at the Air, ſtayeth there, and hardly toucheth it ; whence I may aswell ſay, that the water is more eaſier divided than the Air.

I will not on this occaſion forbear to give warning of another fallacy of theſe perſons, who attribute the reaſon of ſinking or ſwimming to the greater or leſſe Reſiſtance of the Craſſitude of the water againſt Diviſion, making uſe of the example of an Egg, which in ſweet water goeth to the bottom, but in ſalt water ſwims ; and alledging for the cauſe thereof, the faint Reſiſtance of freſh water againſt Diviſion, and the ſtrong Reſiſtance of ſalt water. But if I miſtake not, from the ſame Experiment, we may aswell deduce the quite contrary; namely, that the freſh water is more denſe, and the ſalt more tenuous and ſubtle, ſince an Egg from the bottom of ſalt water ſpeedily aſcends to the top, and divides its Reſiſtance, which it cannot do in the freſh, in whoſe bottom it ſtays, being unable to riſe upwards. Into ſuch like perplexities, do falſe Principles Lead men: but he that rightly Philoſophating, ſhall acknowledge the exceſſes of the Gravities of the Moveables and of the Mediums, to be the Cauſes of thoſe effects, will ſay, that the Egg ſinks to the bottom in freſh water, for that it is more grave than it, and ſwimeth in the ſalt, for that its leſs grave than it : and ſhall without any abſurdity, very ſolidly eſtabliſh his Concluſions.

Therefore the reaſon totally ceaſeth, that *Ariſtotle* ſubjoyns in the Text ſaying ; The things, therefore, which have great breadth remain above, becauſe they comprehend much, and that which is greater, is not caſily divided. Such diſcourſing ceaſeth, I ſay, becauſe its not true, that there is in water or in Air any Reſiſtance of Diviſion ; beſides that the Plate of Lead when it ſtays, hath already divided and penetrated the Craſſitude of the water, and profounded it ſelf ten or twelve times more than its own thickneſs: beſides that ſuch Reſiſtance of Diviſion, were it ſuppoſed to be in the water, could not rationally be affirmed to be more in its ſuperiour parts than in the middle, and lower : but if there were any difference, the inferiour ſhould be the more denſe, ſo that the Plate would be no leſs unable to penetrate the lower, than the ſuperiour parts of the water ; nevertheleſs we ſee that no ſooner do we wet the ſuperiour Superficies of the Board or thin Piece of Wood, but it precipitatly, and without any retenſion, deſcends to the bottom.

Text 45.

I believe not after all this, that any (thinking perhaps thereby to defend *Ariſtotle*) will ſay, that it being true, that the much water reſiſts more than the little, the ſaid Board being put lower deſcendeth, becauſe there remaineth a leſs Maſs of water to be divided by it : becauſe if after the having ſeen the ſame Board ſwim in four Inches of water, and alſo after that in the ſame to ſink, he ſhall try the ſame Experiment upon a profundity of ten or twenty fathom water, he ſhall ſee the very ſelf ſame effect. And here I will take occaſion to remember, for the removall of an Error that is too common; That that Ship or other whatsoever Body, that on the depth of an hundred or a thousand fathom, swims with submerging only six fathom of its own height, [*or in the Sea-dialect, that draws six fathom water*] shall swim in the same manner in water, that hath but six fathom and half an Inch of depth. Nor do I on the other side, think that it can be said, that the superiour parts of the water are the more dense, although a most grave Authour hath esteemed the superiour water in the Sea to be so, grounding his opinion upon its being more salt, than that at the bottom: but I doubt the Experiment, whether hitherto in taking the water from the bottom, the Observatour did not light upon some spring of fresh water there spouting up: but we plainly see on the contrary, the fresh Waters of Rivers to dilate themselves for some miles beyond their place of meeting with the salt water of the Sea, without descending in it, or mixing with it, unless by the intervention of some commotion or turbulency of the Windes.

A Ship that in 100 Fathome water draweth 6 Fathome, shall float in 6 Fathome and ½ an Inch of depth.

But returning to *Aristotle*, I say, that the breadth of Figure hath nothing to do in this business more or less, because the said Plate of Lead, or other Matter, cut into long Slices, swim neither more nor less; and the same shall the Slices do, being cut anew into little pieces, because its not the breadth but the thickness that operates in this business. I say farther, that in case it were really true, that the Renitence to Division were the proper Cause of swimming, the Figures more narrow and short, would much better swim than the more spacious and broad, so that augmenting the breadth of the Figure, the facility of supernatation will be deminished, and decreasing, that this will encrease.

Thickness not breadth of Figure to be respected in Natation.

Were Renitence the cause of Natation, breadth of Figure would hinder the swiming of Bodies.

And for declaration of what I say, consider that when a thin Plate of Lead descends, dividing the water, the Division and discontinuation is made between the parts of the water, invironing the perimeter or Circumference of the said Plate, and according to the bigness greater or lesser of that circuit, it hath to divide a greater or lesser quantity of water, so that if the circuit, suppose of a Board, be ten Feet in sinking it flatways, it is to make the seperation and division, and to so speak, an incission upon ten Feet of water; and likewise a lesser Board that is four Feet in Perimeter, must make an incession of four Feet. This granted, he that hath any knowledge in Geometry, will comprehend, not only that a Board sawed in many long thin pieces, will much better float than when it was entire, but that all Figures, the more short and narrow they be, shall so much the better swim. Let the Board A B C D be, for Example, eight Palmes long, and five broad, its circuit shall be twenty six Palmes; and so many must the incession be, which it shall make in the water to descend therein: but if we do saw ir, as suppose into eight little

pieces

pieces, according to the Lines E F, G H, &c. making ſeven Segments, we muſt adde to the twenty ſix Palmes of the circuit of the whole Board, ſeventy others; whereupon the eight little pieces ſo cut and ſeperated, have to cut ninty ſix Palmes of water. And, if moreover, we cut each of the ſaid pieces into five parts, reducing them into Squares, to the circuit of ninty ſix Palmes, with four cuts of eight Palmes apiece; we ſhall adde alſo ſixty four Palmes, whereupon the ſaid Squares to deſcend in the water, muſt divide one hundred and ſixty Palmes of water, but the Reſiſtance is much greater than that of twenty ſix; therefore to the leſſer Superficies, we ſhall reduce them, ſo much the more eaſily will they float: and the ſame will happen in all other Figures, whoſe Superficies are ſimular amongſt themſelves, but different in bigneſs: becauſe the ſaid Superficies, being either deminiſhed or encreaſed, always diminiſh or encreaſe their Perimeters in ſubduple proportion; to wit, the Reſiſtance that they find in penetrating the water; therefore the little pieces gradually ſwim, with more and more facility as their breadth is leſſened.

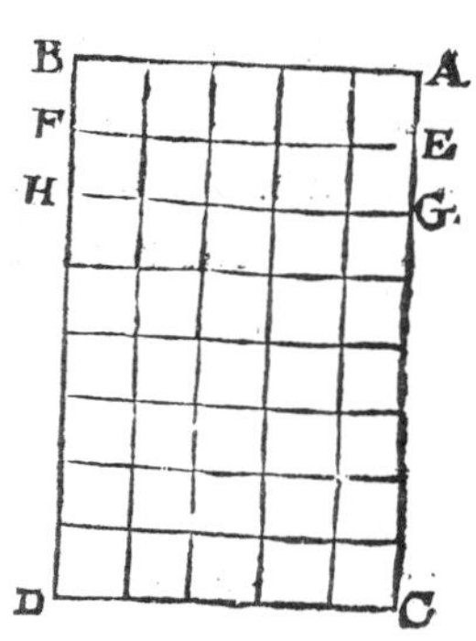

This is manifeſt; for keeping ſtill the ſame height of the Solid, with the ſame proportion as the Baſe encreaſeth or deminiſheth, doth the ſaid Solid alſo encreaſe or diminiſh; whereupon the Solid more diminiſhing than the Circuit, the Cauſe of Submerſion more diminiſheth than the Cauſe of Natation: And on the contrary, the Solid more encreaſing than the Circuit, the Cauſe of Submerſion encreaſeth more, that of Natation leſs.

And this may all be deduced out of the Doctrine of *Ariſtotle* againſt his own Doctrine.

Laſtly, to that which we read in the latter part of the Text, that is to ſay, that we muſt compare the Gravity of the Moveable with the Reſiſtance of the Medium againſt Diviſion, becauſe if the force of the Gravity exceed the Reſiſtance of the *Medium*, the Moveable will deſcend, if not it will float. I need not make any other anſwer, but that which hath been already delivered; namely, that its not the Reſiſtance of abſolute Diviſion, (which neither is in Water nor Air) but the Gravity of the *Medium* that muſt be compared with the Gravity of the Moveables; and if that of the *Medium* be greater, the Moveable ſhall not deſcend, nor ſo much as make a totall Submerſion, but a partiall only: becauſe in the place which it would occupy in the water, there muſt not remain a Body that weighs leſs than a like quantity of water: but if the Moveable be more grave, it ſhall deſcend to the bottom, and poſſeſs a place where it is more conformable

Lib. 4. c. 6. Text 45.

for it to remain, than another Body that is leſs grave. And this is the only true proper and abſolute Cauſe of Natation and Submerſion, ſo that nothing elſe hath part therein : and the Board of the Adverſaries ſwimmeth, when it is conjoyned with as much Air, as, together with it, doth form a Body leſs grave than ſo much water as would fill the place that the ſaid Compound occupyes in the water ; but when they ſhall demit the ſimple Ebony into the water, according to the Tenour of our Queſtion, it ſhall alwayes go to the bottom, though it were as thin as a Paper.

FINIS.

Textual corrections and emendations

1. Lines not appearing in the original editions

Page	*Line*	*Page*	*Line*	*Page*	*Line*	*Page*	*Line*
5	20	9	27	26	12	52	1
5	26	11	1	45	15	52	4
5	34	12	1	46	29	52	27
6	4	13	1	48	1	53	27
6	14	14	1	48	21	54	21
6	17	15	15	50	1	54	25
7	5	16	1	50	16	55	1
7	36	18	9	51	9	58	8

2. Lines appearing in italics which should be in roman type

5	21-22	13	2- 4	48	2- 4	52	5- 7
5	27-29	14	2-10	48	22-30	52	28-31
5	35-37	15	16-19	49	27-28	53	28-29
6	5- 7	16	2- 7	50	2- 6	54	22-24
6	15-16	18	10-11	50	11-13	54	26-29
7	6- 7	26	13-15	50	17-19	55	2- 5
7	37-40	45	16-19	51	10-13	58	9-11
11	2- 9	46	30-35	52	2- 3	62	37-39
12	2- 7	47	38				

3. Lines appearing in roman type which should be in italics

6	18-20	21	34-39	65	40-42	66	1- 4
9	28-35						

4. Omissions, errors, and suggested readings in the text

Page	*Line*	*Read:*
1	29	. . . in its Orbe 4 *gr.* 13 *min.* or very near
2	5	ments. For such exactnesse . . .
2	19	. . . Body, which changing position in that, propounds
3	7	. . . others. And because . . .
4	11	. . . impossible. I concluded . . .
4	12	was in no sort a Cause . . .
4	16	. . . I supposed that those which held other-
4	30	. . . Conclusion. Which, if . . .

Page	*Line*	*Read:*
4	38	I can possibly, it . . .
5	6	. . . BODIES: reprehended afterwards
5	7	. . . if I erre not, incorrectly, as below for
6	8	. . . weigh absolutely more than a
6	12	. . . from the Science of Mechanicks . . .
6	16	. . . . equall Forces and Moments
6	28	. . . *and let us consider* . . .
7	18	Velocity of the motion is . . .
8	5	. . . that by necessity float on the
8	7	. . . Mass rising above . . .
9	7	is not impossible that a Solid
9	18	what difficult . . .
9	23	. . . a right Cylinder, or . . .
10	6	*LG shall return* . . .
10	7	. . . *it was contained be-*
10	16	. . . *Water raised LG* . . .
10	20	. . . *Water to be according* . . .
10	21	. . . *HIK to be then taken out and*
10	24-25	. . . *inferiour EIK, the common part EN being removed, and* . . .
11	30	. . . Water to the space of lifting of the
11	37	. . . only 1/24 of a foot.
11	38	. . . difficult to understand according to its true
12	38	and what shall be above . . .
14	17	that any little quantity . . .
14	21-23	. . . GD; and the proportion of the Mass BG to the Mass GD taken with the proportion of the Mass GD to the Mass AF gives the proportion of the Mass BG to the Mass AF, therefore . . .
16	37	. . . Mass than that. Which we thus
17	14	*draw from errour some Practical Mechanicians* . . .
17	15	. . . *unto the very broad*
17	17	. . . *infused into this, unto* . . .
17	25-27	. . . *only to QO, and shall then consider what the Water CL will have done; this, to give place* . . . [Note: Diagram lacks points F, H, and O, opposite to E, G, and Q horizontally.]
17	33	. . . *Funnell LC*
17	35	. . . *LC. But in* . . .
18	21	. . . water. And though . . .
18	22	. . . which equaleth
18	29	the Horizon and parallel to each other, that comprehend
18	33	. . . Rest of various Solid Bodies in [i.e., state of rest of . . .]
19	8	nother Solid, provided that . . .
19	20	. . . places, provided that they
20	11	. . . but this property
20	15	. . . to the domain of the Elements, so
20	20	. . . who did not take pains to overthrow the
20	30-31	. . . all authority in persuasion, . . .
20	43	than water, and hence Earth is less grave than water. If this . . .
21	33	other phenomenon could have induced him to do this.
22	9	easily reduced into any shape, may . . .
22	25	. . . follow, and is on the contrary . . .
22	40	. . . Cavities, it may very well be that then such compound

Page	*Line*	*Read:*
		becomes heavier than water in the manner in which, the air leaving the glass vial and being followed by water,
23	7	like as before (according to the same doctrine) it did swim.
23	8	As to that finally which was objected in the fourth place . . .
23	9	. . . Aristotle, they
24	end	Impetus, and slowly mingles with the other air.
25	20	Resistance to Division . . .
26	1	. . . despise those benefits, though very tenuous, which
26	6	. . . any place within water, if its Gravity
26	18	into any other Figure, the same [Solid] in the same water shall
26	19	. . . Motion by the breadth or by o-
26	21	The breadth of the Figure . . .
26	27	in particular a thin chip of Ebony . . .
26	32	of the Figure, unable . . .
26	35-36	. . . in which I shall use my ingenuity to make it manifest that I am on the right side.
27	2	. . . Experiment with materials
27	14	shapes.
27	18	and being *in specie* very little inferiour in Gravity
28	16	. . . apt to overcome the resistance of the viscosity of the water,
28	18	. . . Levity, to overcome the resistance of the Crassitude . . .
28	24	Density or Crassitude of the water.
28	31	a blade of grass, have illustrated . . .
28	33	the other hand, of the same . . .
28	36	. . . Lath or chip . . .
28	38	from the chip . . .
29	14	than Steel for finding . . .
30	29	meth the contrary of this which Experience shews me.
31	11	. . . namely a handsbreadth or more
31	13	. . . by the breadth of the Base,
31	42	. . . Wax, and mixing it with
33	9	. . . But these Boards that slowly . . .
34	1	. . . the same bignesse goes to the bottom,
34	26	. . . make a plate of Wax, or thin
34	34	. . . other plates and Boards of
34	39	to swim. What then shall we say of it? I for my part should say that it was the contrary of whatever caused the sinking, inasmuch as the sinking and the floating are contrary effects, and the causes of contrary effects must be contraries.
35	2	. . . it did sink, more
35	3	. . . water, but less. But this new lightness cannot depend on the shape, both because shape neither adds nor detracts from the weight, and because in the little board there is no change of shape whatever when it goes to the bottom, from that which it had while it was floating.
35	7	first, see how sound the assertion . . .
35	13	the said Plates, within the profundity . . .
35	14	. . . shall be of material more grave
35	16-17	. . . of the surrounding water many times more than the thickness . . .
36	10	are my Antagonists, in our Question we . . .
36	32	. . . Water by simply wetting it slightly: for I will
36	34	. . . which drops, if not conjoyned with

Page	*Line*	*Read:*
36	35	. . . shall not bear down on it so as
38	13	such wetting did not trouble them in the beginning
38	16	wherein it would be too simple-minded to require . . .
38	20	Board of Ebony even upon the superiour . . .
38	25	. . . to be driven
38	37	Haply, some of . . .
39	10	. . . making withal its Superficies . . .
39	12	. . . remaining uncovered only a little . . .
39	25	. . . not without some little violence . . .
39	43	that such Contact, when it is very exact, may not be a . . .
40	1	. . . I say that there is no use having
40	29	. . . Bodies that stick in the water . . .
41	26	by the waters before the Ship . . .
41	32-33	. . . must those waters make, that following the poop do run from the end parts of the Ship . . .
42	4- 5	. . . *Mass should, to some sensible force, remain immoveable* . . .
42	29	. . . *Silver or other cold* . . .
42	30-31	. . . *two parts, feel not only the resistance that is felt in the* . . .
44	20	. . . for the investigating of the Cause of that
47	catchword	Theoreme
48	6	. . . water, and given moreover the greatest . . .
48	9	. . . upon the water, if we should make
48	22	The breadth of figure . . .
49	2	depends the determining what . . .
50	9	. . . Figures the properties are
50	11	. . . a Piramide or cone of any . . .
51	19	. . . third part of the altitude of the Piramide
52	13	. . . they shall leave above them equall
55	2	. . . to form Solid . . .
55	7	Solid Figures that terminate in . . .
55	21	. . . therefore, that terminate
55	27	. . . Cones and thin Piramids. Touch-
57	1	. . . yet the point stands . . .
57	18	. . . the Cone AST is
58	6- 7	. . . they terminate, being . . .
58	25	four inches thick . . .
58	30	. . . Air, which together with the
58	38-39	. . . Example, an inch thick and four inches square, and should . . .
59	22-23	. . . of my Opponents, whether Figure . . .
59	31	pinion, I will hang from a small thread . . .
59	33	. . . to the other arm I by degrees
59	39	. . . Weights on the other arm, till . . .
60	36-38	As printed. (Salusbury's translation is not in error on the grounds supposed by some previous owner of the volume, whose suggested readings are based on a misapprehension of Galileo's meaning. This may be paraphrased as follows: "Air resists and 'weighs' downward in water precisely as much as water would resist and 'weigh' upward in air"; that is, as compared with its weight *in vacuo*.)
61	14-15	. . . think of, to show the truth of the side I have undertaken to defend. It remains . . .
61	18-19	. . . about the simple moving or not moving upwards . . .

Page	*Line*	*Read:*
61	25	. . . Figure, to be a part of this operation.
61	40	Figures their being the Causes of moving simply, but yet not their
62	17	it is, that the broad and thinne . . .
63	8	. . . it is not suitable to inverte them.
63 to 64	42 to 1	"Figure is the Cause *secundum quid* of not sinking; but now if it is asked for what Cause a thin Plate of Lead goes not to the bottom, it shall be answered that this proceeds from its Figure": reasoning which would be indecent to a Child, let alone to Aristotle, for
64	4	. . . have writ that "Figure is in a
64	6	. . . Figure swims." But if we take
64	8	. . . come in very appositely . . .
64	10	. . . say thus much:
64	11	"Figures are . . .
64	13	it be so, it is asked whence it comes about that a Plate of
64	14	. . . doth swim, etc." . . .
64	18	. . . hath no action in this effect.
64	32	But that he hath . . .
64	33	. . . he proposeth, I will not undertake
64	39	. . . than to the contra-
64	44	lesser things, and less grave, be . . .
65	1	. . . Now this I doubt, and indeed am certain
65	42	*not a small one; for then I ask what he intended of a small one,*
66	1	*and one must reply, that . . .*
66	14	us, that that does not happen, and not only in Air, but not even in water, in
66	16	muddy it, whose smallness is such that they are not observable, save
68	30	. . . should uphold in water a Body,
69	33	to overthrow Democritus, was . . .
69	39	clare what thing Gravity and Levity were; that is, the Cause of
69	41	. . . this to Fire by which . . .
69	42	the Earth by which . . .
70	8	. . . is never seen in any case . . .
70	11	. . . erre not, Aristotle's manner of deduction
70	13	. . . force be turned back against himself . . .
71	36	. . . thin Leaves and fine powder, not only swims in
71	39	. . . less: and this he
72	12	the water is more difficult to divide than the Air? . . .
72	36	. . . sinks not, through inability . . .
72	37	. . . that if they drive it under water . . .
72	40	to say that "this Solid . . .
72	42	divided," concludes . . .
73	22	Text saying, "The things . . .
73	24	is not easily divided." Such reasoning fails, I say . . .
74	21	squares, because it's not . . .
74	28	And for explanation of what I say . . .
74	43	and so long must the incision be . . .
75	11	but the Resistance of one hundred and sixty is much greater . . .
75	19	. . . gradually swim with more
75	34	descend, if not it will float, I need not
75	36	. . . (which exists neither in Water nor
75	43	. . . it is more conformable to nature

Explanatory notes

All notes are keyed by indication of the subject phrase or passage in the text.

PAGE 1

Line 20 Saturn . . . tricorporeall

Galileo's telescope failed to resolve the rings of Saturn, and he interpreted the appearance as showing Saturn to have two small stationary satellites close beside it.

Line 21 Medicean Planets.

Galileo so named the four satellites of Jupiter seen by him, in honor of the ruling house of Tuscany. The calculation of their periodic movements was set as a challenge problem to mathematicians in the *Sidereus Nuncius*, but none had up to this time published a solution. In confirmation of Galileo's statement that he had solved the problem while at Rome in 1611, there is a letter from G. B. Agucchi dated 9 September 1611, asking Galileo to refresh his memory concerning the sizes of the orbits. Galileo's side of the ensuing correspondence is not preserved, but it appears that he was reluctant to give out his data prior to publication; instead he gave merely the relative dimensions of the orbits. From these, with the help of Galileo's original observations in the *Sidereus Nuncius* and further observations of his own, Agucchi was able to deduce a set of periodic times very close to those set forth here by Galileo. These he communicated to Galileo on 14 October 1611, with a request for confirmation. From another letter, dated 29 October, it can be deduced that Galileo had promptly confirmed Agucchi's findings except for the largest orbit, in which Galileo found one revolution to consume sixteen days eighteen hours in place of Agucchi's sixteen days twenty hours.

PAGE 2

Line 14 continue the observation

Galileo's observations of the satellites continued until 1619, at which time he despaired of ever attaining complete precision such as would be necessary for the utilization of their eclipses in determining longitudes at sea. His difficulties were due at least in part to phenomena of which he could not have been aware, such as perturbations introduced by the gravitational effects of the sun and of the other planets, and the effect of the finite speed of light upon the apparent times of the eclipses of the satellites throughout the year.

Line 18 some obscure spots

Galileo's first published remarks about sunspots in this place were made with great caution, particularly in view of the fact that a German astronomer (the Jesuit Father Christopher Scheiner) had already published an account of them in which he attributed the appearances to the circulation of small planets about or beneath the sun. Early in 1612, after recovering from a long illness and while the *Discourse* was in the hands of the printer, Galileo conducted a series of careful observations which enabled him to refute utterly the contentions of Scheiner. Thus in the second edition of the *Discourse* he was able to insert the more positive assertions printed below in italics. (An abridged translation of Galileo's book on sunspots published in 1613 is given in *Discoveries*, pp. 87-144.)

Line 20

Alcinoos
The dictum of Alcinous, that in order to philosophize one's mind must first of all be free, had become closely associated with the defense of Copernicus, having been cited by Rheticus in the first published summary of the new world system and by Kepler in his endorsement of the *Sidereus Nuncius*.

PAGE 5
Line 7

A very grave author
Francesco Buonamico, teacher of philosophy at the University of Pisa during Galileo's student days there, and author of a lengthy treatise on motion. Criticisms of Buonamico's doctrines occur at pp. 19ff and 62ff, below.

Line 9

a different Method
Though Galileo's conclusions in hydrostatics and mechanics agreed with those of Archimedes, whom he greatly admired, he preferred not to utilize the rigid method of mathematical deduction introduced by the Syracusan into physics. Rather, Galileo appeals to induction from observation and experiment in support of his reasoning throughout the *Discourse*. Striking evidences of this predilection of Galileo's will also be found in his other works; for example, in the earlier *Mechanics* (Engl. tr. pp. 154-155) and in the final *Two New Sciences* (p. 110). At the same time it is interesting to note that Galileo criticized William Gilbert for too much reliance upon experiment alone and not enough upon mathematical reasoning (*Dialogue*, tr. Drake, p. 406). It is Galileo's insistence on uniting the two methods that entitles him to be considered the first truly modern physicist.

PAGE 6
Line 18

moment
This definition of moment in terms of weight and speed enabled Galileo to make effective use of the principle of virtual velocities in his analysis of hydrostatic problems, as he had previously done for simple machines in his *Mechanics*. The defense of his definition, added in italics, was in direct reply to a criticism by the "Unknown Academician"; see Introduction, p. XXII.

PAGE 7
Line 34

Galileo expressly credits Aristotle with the principle of virtual velocities, though many historians suppose him to have borrowed it from the medieval writer Jordanus Nemorarius. At Galileo's hands the principle became a powerful weapon of analysis through the quantification and refinement of a previously existing vague and intuitive notion. The ancient statement occurs in the pseudo-Aristotelian *Mechanical Problems*, §3, where it is applied solely to the lever, without restriction to small initial movements, and without application to conditions of equilibrium. In the succeeding paragraphs the reader will perceive the great generality with which Galileo was able to apply the principle to hydrostatic problems.

PAGE 13
Marginal Note

Salusbury's gloss here contains what is probably the first occurrence in English of the term "specific gravity."

PAGE 17
Line 18

not without admiration of some
The so-called hydrostatic paradox had previously been described and explained by Stevin in terms of distribution of pressures and in a manner worthy of Archimedes himself. Stevin's treatment stands in interesting contrast with that of Galileo, whose

observations here are adduced in the spirit of the Aristotelian work mentioned above. It was the wedding of these static and dynamic approaches to mechanical problems in the seventeenth century that gave rise to modern conceptions of mechanics.

PAGE 29
Line 14 than Steel
That is, it is easier to fashion wax "knives" of various shapes than steel knives.

PAGE 30
Line 41 all their thickness under the Surface
Here begins Galileo's discussion of the floating of thin lamina of materials having greater specific gravity than water — a discussion which down to this day has been insufficiently appreciated, and even at times ridiculed. We know that the effect takes place by reason of the surface tension of water, and since Galileo did not form that concept, it has been frequently assumed that his discussion of the observed phenomena was without merit. That opinion was strengthened by a general misapprehension of Galileo's remark (discussed in a later note) about a sort of magnetic effect between the air and the dry surface.

Galileo's analysis of the depth to which floating bodies of varying densities will depress the surface of the water is acute and ingenious, and by no means conceptually unsound, though his assertion that the floating body in this situation is "a compound of air with the floating body" may strike one at first as bizarre. If so, the reader should refer to Galileo's discussion (pp. 20-21) of full and empty earthenware vessels, from which he doubtless took the clue to the present analysis. Confronted with an apparent exception to the rule of Archimedes, Galileo approached its explanation by first observing the actual phenomena much more closely than his adversaries (who presented it to refute him) had done. Partisans of the view that Galileo himself was not much of an experimentalist, and that he justified his conclusions *a posteriori* principally from experiments he had performed in thought alone, can scarcely account in that way for the observations recorded in this discussion.

PAGE 31
Line 11 a hand or more
That is, *palmo*, or approximately four inches.

PAGE 38
Line 40 a kind of Magnetick vertue
Galileo is speaking here of those who disagree with him and who say he speaks "as if I would in a certain sense allow the air" such a power. The reference was to an event in one of the oral debates in which this remark was made by an important personage, possibly Giovanni de' Medici. For tactical reasons, Galileo did not ridicule the idea but adapted it to his own purposes in the manner set forth in the text. Yet the word "magnetic," introduced to avoid offending a particular adversary, became at once the source of misunderstanding and controversy in his own time, let alone in succeeding generations. Here is what Galileo had to say to one such critic:

"First of all, your Excellency names as introduced by me a certain magnetic power, with which I would have it that the air, adhering to the ebony chip, sustains it without permitting it to submerge under the water. Now in this matter it is good that you should know that this term "magnetic power" is not mine, but that of an important gentleman, out of accordance with my views and adhering to the opponents. He, being present on a certain occasion when it pleased their Serene Highnesses to see some experiments on this subject, where some of my other adversaries were present . . . broke in to say to me in the presence of their Highnesses and many other gentlemen: 'Then you wish to give to the air a magnetic attraction, by means of which it can by mere contact govern the bodies contiguous to it?' Whereupon later, coming in my *Discourse* to an occasion on which I mentioned the way in which the air arrests the chips heavier than water, I said, addressing my adversaries (of whom, as I said, more than one was present at the said experiments), 'and this, my distinguished opponents, is that magnetic power with which the air, etc.' — alluding to that attribution of magnetic power that had been proffered in the presence of their Highnesses. And now what? If in that place, explaining at great length the cause of that adherence of the air to the chip, I referred this simply to intimate contact, and adduced examples of other smooth surfaces fitting precisely together, without ever mentioning magnetic force, then why should there be attributed to me that which I do not say? Why replace what I said, in clear and fully developed terms, by a single word spoken metaphorically? Spoken, I say, in order to push it back upon its introducers, so that they would know that it was not deemed by me to be true." (Letter to Tolomeo Nozzolini, *Opere* IV, 298-299.)

Galileo's observations and theories concerning wetting and the motion of fluids adjacent to moving solid bodies were developed further in *The Assayer*, while his views as to the forces involved in perfect contact of solid bodies were set forth more fully in the *Two New Sciences*. See, for example, *The Controversy on the Comets of 1618*, Philadelphia, 1960, pp. 280-281; *Two New Sciences*, pp. 11ff.

PAGE 43
Line 22

will not happen, in case
That is, no resistance will be detected provided that the experiment is meticulously performed.

PAGE 52
Line 28

A piramide or cone
This theorem is inherently so implausible to common sense that one can hardly escape the conclusion that Galileo actually performed the experiment before publishing the conclusion. Without preparing wax cones as Galileo did, the reader who wishes to verify it may easily make the test by using some roughly conical chocolate chips, such as those which are sold for use in baking cookies. No particular care is required in placing these in the water, base up or base down, to see the effect which Galileo describes.

PAGE 55
Line 35

almost impossible to effect
It should be noted that Galileo does not assert that he himself had succeeded in this, whereas he did assert (p. 27) that a preparation could be made such that its rising or sinking would be determined by the removal or addition of a single grain of lead. Though the view is frequently expressed that Galileo was inclined to exaggerate his experimental claims, he was for the most part a prudent reporter except in works of a literary character designed more to attract interest than to expound minor difficulties.

PAGE 60
Line 22

make me feel with my hand
A colloquial Italian expression, meaning "make evident to my senses." This entire argument, ingeniously turning the tables on his opponents, once more evidences the multitude of observational phenomena which Galileo had always at hand, usually of a kind that can hardly have originated merely in his imagination.

PAGE 70
Line 23

the greater specificall Gravity
The language of this passage suggests that Galileo had not, at the time of writing the *Discourse*, reached his ultimate conclusion that differences in speed of free fall observed in bodies of different materials are due to the resistance of the air, and would vanish in a vacuum. The effect mentioned here (equal speed of fall of bodies of a given material regardless of weight) agrees with the result supposed to have been demonstrated from the Leaning Tower of Pisa, and with conclusions set forth in Galileo's *De motu* about 1590, at which time his analysis of the phenomena was based essentially on hydrostatic principles.

Index